S0-BBB-458

A Closer Look

Procedure

1. **Collaborate** Work with a partner. Use a plastic knife to cut a thin slice of the mushroom cap. The slice should be as thin as possible and about 2 cm long.

2. **Experiment** Use tweezers to place the mushroom slice on a plastic slide. Place a slide cover over the sample.

3. **Observe** Take turns using the microscope. Observe the fine details of the sample at different magnifications.

4. **Record Data** In the space below, carefully sketch an example or section of the sample. Add labels for structures that you can identify or recognize.

5. Repeat steps 3 and 4 with each of the prepared slides your teacher provides. **Safety:** Wash your hands after handling the slides.

Observations will vary depending upon the preparation of the sample and the magnification used. Be certain students have used consistent labels.

Conclusion

On the lines below, write the answers to the questions.

1. **Compare** All the slides you observed contained organisms that are alive or were once alive. Review your sketches and compare them. List ways that the organisms are alike and different.

   Sample answer: Their size, shape, color, and cell structure

   are different.

   _____

2. **Infer** Using one characteristic, explain how to separate these organisms into two groups.

   Accept any reasonable response, such as groups based on

   plant-like versus animal-like characteristics, presence or

   absence of cilia, or definite shape versus amorphous shape.

   _____

Investigate More!

Research Today's system of classifying living things began with the work of Swedish physician Carolus Linnaeus. Research Linnaeus's life and his contributions to science.

Dichotomous Key

Procedure

1. **Observe** Look carefully at the photos. You are going to classify them with a dichotomous key.

2. **Classify** Record your classification in the graphic organizer below. Which of the items come from trees and which do not? Fill in the names of the items in the right-hand side boxes on the flow chart.

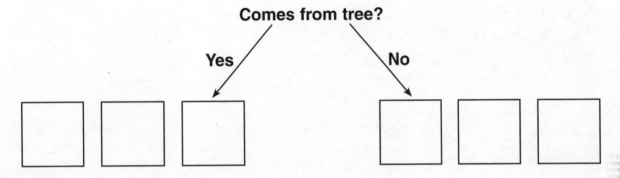

Further divisions may include seeds/no seeds, color distinctions, and texture distinctions. Each division should identify a logical characteristic.

3. **Classify** Choose the group of items that come from trees. Divide it again by a characteristic that some items have and others do not. Record the names of the items on the key. Continue to divide the group until an item is by itself. When you have completed one side of the key, do the same thing with the group of items that do not come from trees.

4. Share your dichotomous key with your teacher and classmates. Explain how you classified the items.

Conclusion

Write the answers to the questions below.

1. **Collaborate** Work with other students to collect more examples of plants. On a separate sheet of paper, develop a more detailed dichotomous key based on characteristics of each plant. Keys should have a wider range of traits than those used for the first activity. Traits may include color, leaf or petal patterns, and surface texture.

2. **Infer** Think about your observations in developing your dichotomous key. What do you think scientists may use as characteristics to further classify plants?

    Sample answer: Scientists often use internal characteristics and genetic factors, as well as external traits like leaf shape and color to classify plants.

Investigate More!

Research Collect leaf samples from your neighborhood. Determine the type of plant by using a reference book or the Internet. Make a poster that shows each leaf and an explanation of how you found out what type of plant it came from.

4
Use with page A15

Organizing Animals

Procedure

1. **Observe** Use the hand lens to carefully examine each animal specimen and picture. Pay close attention to how they are alike and how they are different.

2. **Record Data** Record each specimen's characteristics in the chart below. Describe the similarities and differences as you record your observations.

Specimen	Characteristics

3. **Classify** Look at the characteristics you recorded. Are there two main groups into which you can sort all the specimens? Sort them and name the two groups. Record your classification on the lines below.

Sample answers: animals that walk versus those that fly; _____

animals that live on land versus those that live in water _____

4. **Classify** How are the specimens in each group similar to each other? How are they different? Sort the specimens into additional groups based on characteristics they share. Record your additional classifications on the lines below.

Sample answer: animals that eat plants versus those that

eat other animals

Conclusion

Write the answers to the questions below.

1. **Infer** All of the specimens you studied are animals. What characteristics do you think all animals have in common?

   Answers may include being able to move, being able to eat,

   and having many cells.

2. **Communicate** On a separate sheet of paper, make a poster or chart showing the specimens you have grouped. Explain to your teacher and class why you organized the groups as you did. Any logical grouping is acceptable.

Investigate More!

Design an Experiment How picky are the wild birds in your neighborhood? Will they eat any kind of birdseed, or only certain kinds? Design an experiment to find out. Have your teacher approve your procedure before you perform it.

Use with page A27

Building a Plant Cell

Procedure

1. **Observe** Use the hand lens to carefully examine the photographs of the plant cells. Also look at the diagram of a plant cell on page A47 of your book.

2. **Analyze Data** Look at the similarities between the plant cells. Identify the parts that all plant cells have. Write these parts on the lines below.

   Sample answers: chloroplasts, a cell wall, a nucleus, etc.
   _____

   _____

3. **Communicate** Use your observations to develop a plan to make a model of a plant cell with the materials you have. Show your plan to your teacher. Discuss your idea.

   _____

   _____

   _____

   _____

4. **Use Models** Use the materials to make your model of the cell. Name each part using the index cards. Describe what you think each part's function is. Use one index card for each part of the cell. Describe your model on the lines below.

   Students' models should include mitochondria, vacuoles,
   _____

   a cell wall, chloroplasts, cytoplasm, a nucleus, a cell
   _____

   membrane, and Golgi bodies.
   _____

Conclusion

Write the answers to the questions below.

1. **Observe** Although all plant cells share certain structures, the cells from different plants are not exactly alike. How did observing different types of plant cells help you plan your model?

   Sample answer: Cell parts can have different shapes and

   sizes in different cells. Some plant cells have more of

   certain structures than other plant cells.

   _____

2. **Infer** Look at your model. Why do you think plants have a thick wall surrounding each cell?

   Thick walls help support the plant cells and the plant. Thick

   walls also protect the plant cells.

3. **Infer** How did making your cell model help you draw conclusions about the functions of certain parts of plant cells?

   Sample answer: Putting water in a vacuole shows that

   vacuoles store liquid in cells. Batteries are an energy

   source, and mitochondria are a cell's energy source.

   _____

Investigate More!

Ask Questions Look at a microscopic view of a mushroom cell and compare it with a plant leaf cell. What structure or structures are missing from the mushroom cell? Why do you think leaves are green, but mushrooms are not?

8

Use with page A45

Moving Through!

Procedure

1. **Measure** Wet the dialysis tubing. Tie one end of the tubing like a balloon. Fill a beaker with 100 mL of tap water. Add a spoonful of starch and stir.

2. Pour the starch mixture into the dialysis tubing and tie the opened end.

3. **Predict** Mixing in iodine will cause a starch solution to turn dark blue-black. Predict what will happen when you place the dialysis tubing in contact with the iodine solution. Write your prediction on the lines below. **Safety:** Do not taste or swallow iodine or other investigation materials. Keep your hands away from your mouth and avoid getting the iodine solution on your clothes. Wear goggles to protect your eyes.

4. **Observe** Pour the iodine solution into the second beaker and place dialysis tubing inside. In the chart below, record your observations every two minutes.

Time	Observations
2 min	
4 min	
6 min	
8 min	
10 min	

9
Use with page A53

Name _____ Date _____

Conclusion

Write the answers to the questions below.

1. **Use Models** In this experiment, you modeled a cell and saw how substances can move in and out by diffusion. Which cell part did the dialysis tubing represent?

   the cell membrane
   _____

2. **Infer** How do materials pass into and out of a cell?

   through the cell membrane
   _____

   _____

3. **Infer** How do the results explain why large organisms need a digestive system and circulatory system?

   _____

   _____

   _____

Investigate More!

Design an Experiment See if other solutions can diffuse through a plastic bag. Design an experiment using food coloring in the plastic bag. Talk with your teacher about your plan.

Controlling Bacteria

Procedure

1. **Measure** Fill the measuring cup with hot water from the faucet. Add the bouillon cube and wait for it to dissolve. Divide the solution equally among the three cups. **Safety:** The water must be hot enough to dissolve the bouillon. Do not burn yourself.

2. **Experiment** Add one spoonful of vinegar to the first cup. Using the masking tape and pen, mark the cup "Vinegar." Add one spoonful of salt to the second cup. Mark that cup "Salt." Do not add anything to the third cup. Mark that cup "Control." Cover the three cups and store them in a warm place.

3. **Compare** Observe the cups after two, three, and four days. Compare how clear the water is in the different cups.

Sample		Observations
Vinegar	2 days	
	3 days	
	4 days	
Salt	2 days	
	3 days	
	4 days	
Control	2 days	
	3 days	
	4 days	

4. **Record Data** Record your observations in the chart above. Which cup had the clearest water?

the cup with vinegar
_____

Which cup had the cloudiest water?

the control
_____

Conclusion

Write the answers to the questions below.

1. **Analyze Data** Like all organisms, bacteria need the right environments to survive. Look at the data you recorded. Describe how each cup looks. How does bacterial growth affect water clarity?

   Sample answer: The cup to which nothing was added is the

   cloudiest, so the greatest bacterial growth occurred in this

   cup. Adding salt reduces bacterial growth. Adding vinegar

   reduces bacterial growth even more.

   _____

2. **Infer** Review the data you collected. What conclusions can you draw about the effect of salt and vinegar on bacterial growth?

   Salt and vinegar control the growth of harmful bacteria in

   food.

   _____

Investigate More!

Research Bacteria in water can cause disease. Research some waterborne diseases. How do town officials make sure the drinking water is safe? Compare U.S. methods to those used in poorer countries.

New Plants!

Procedure

1. **Observe** Examine the spider plant. Observe the different structures you find.

2. **Record Data** In the space below, make a drawing of the leaves of the plant. Write any observations on the lines below.

_____

_____

3. **Measure** Cut off a stem, about 8 cm long, with a small cluster of leaves at the end. Place the stem in a jar filled with water.

4. **Observe** Each day for several days, examine the stem. Note any changes or new growth. Refill the jar with water as necessary.

5. **Record Data** Write your observations on the lines below.

_____

_____

_____

_____

Conclusion

Write the answers to the questions below.

1. **Infer** Based on your observations, how do you think the stem began to grow?

   The stem grew with the constant supply of water and

   sunlight.

2. **Compare and Contrast** How is this form of reproduction different from reproduction with flowers and seeds?

   It is faster. The plant didn't produce flowers or seeds.

3. **Hypothesize** What do you think would happen if you planted the new roots in soil? Explain.

   Sample answer: The new plant would continue to grow.

4. **Infer** How do you think spider plants reproduce in the wild?

   Sample answer: If the long stems grow along the ground,

   they may grow roots and become new plants.

Investigate More!

Design an Experiment Which plant parts can be cut away and grown into new plants? How large must a cutting be to survive? Design an experiment to help answer either of these questions. Run the experiment with your teacher's permission.

Name _____ Date _____

Split Your Sides

Procedure

1. **Collaborate** Work with a partner. On a large sheet of paper, draw and label six circles.

2. **Use Models** Cut six pieces of yarn of one color: two 2 cm long, two 4 cm long, and two 6 cm long. These pieces of yarn represent three pairs of chromosomes. Place the pairs in the circle labeled *immature female sex cell*.

3. Repeat step 2 with the other color of yarn and place the pairs in the circle labeled *immature male sex cell*. In the space below, draw your model and label it *Before Splitting*.

4. **Experiment** Split each pair of chromosomes in the immature female sex cell and put one chromosome in each of its egg cells. Repeat the process with the immature male sex cell and its sperm cells.

5. **Record Data** Tape the pieces of yarn to the paper in their new positions. In the space below, draw your model and label it *After Splitting*.

Conclusion

Write the answers to the questions below.

1. **Compare** How does the arrangement of chromosomes in your model before splitting compare with that after splitting?

   Before splitting, each cell had three pairs of chromosomes, or a total of six chromosomes. After splitting, each daughter cell had half that number, or a total of three chromosomes.

2. **Infer** How are egg cells and sperm cells like the sex cells that they come from? How are egg cells and sperm cells different from the sex cells that they come from?

   Egg cells are produced by a female and contain her chromosomes. Sperm cells are produced by a male and contain his chromosomes. Both egg and sperm cells contain only half as many chromosomes as their parent cell.

Investigate More!

Design an Experiment Make a new model to explore what would happen if an egg cell and a sperm cell combined to form a new cell. How would the new cell be similar to and different from the original immature sex cells?

Student Resources
16
Use with page A87

Here's Looking at You!

Procedure

1. **Collaborate** Work in a small group. Record your observations in the chart below.

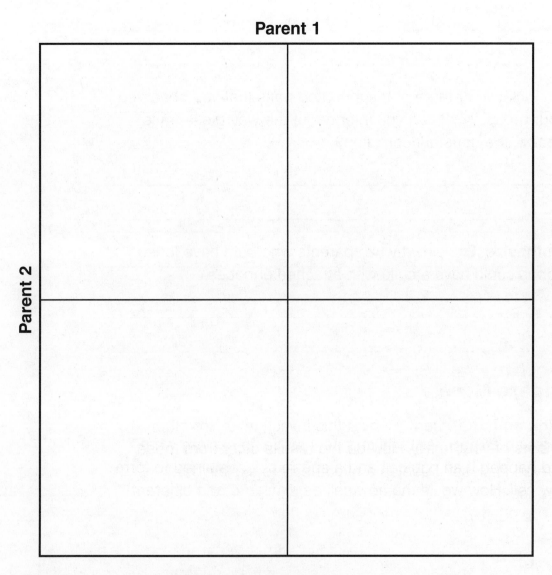

Parent 1

Parent 2

2. **Observe** Using the Inherited Traits key, identify which members of your group have the traits illustrated on the key.

3. **Communicate** Share your results with the other small groups.

4. **Record Data** In your chart, record the number of students in the class who do or do not have the traits listed.

Use with page A101

Conclusion

Write the answers to the questions below.

1. **Analyze Data** For each pair of traits, which of the two appears more often among the members of your class? On a separate sheet of paper, create a bar graph to organize your data.

   Answers will depend on the makeup of the class.

   _____

2. **Infer** Pick two or three of the inherited traits that you observed in your group. What can you infer about the way these traits appear in the general population?

   Sample answer: These traits are quite common in the

   general population.

3. **Hypothesize** Explain why two parents who both have loose earlobes could have a child with attached earlobes.

   The parents would both be hybrid for earlobe type.

   _____

Investigate More!

Design an Experiment Repeat this investigation for other members of your family. How do the results differ from those observed in class? Develop a hypothesis to explain the differences.

Find Out About Fossils

Procedure

1. **Observe** Examine one of the fossils provided to you by your teacher. Look at the shape, structure, texture, and length of the fossil. Record your observations in the chart below.

	Fossil 1	Fossil 2
Shape		
Structure		
Texture		
Length		

2. **Measure** With a metric ruler, measure the length of the fossil and record the data in your chart.

3. **Observe** Reexamine the fossil with a hand lens and record any features you did not notice before.

4. **Use Models** Draw the fossil in the space below, labeling all the details and features you have found.

5. **Observe** Repeat steps 1–4 for the second fossil.

Use with page A117

Conclusion

Write the answers to the questions below.

1. **Infer** Based on your observations, what do you think the fossils are made of?

   The fossils are probably made of rock. However, amber and
   petrified wood are also fossils.

2. **Compare** How are the two fossils similar? How are they different?

   Encourage teams to exchange drawings of fossils to
   broaden the base of comparison. Students should refer to
   characteristics such as size, shape, structure, texture, and
   type of organism.

3. **Hypothesize** What do you think each of the original organisms was? Explain.

   Answers should be based on observations.

4. **Infer** What other facts or ideas about the organisms can you infer? Discuss your reasoning.

   Sample answer: I can infer the environment in which each
   organism lived based on the environment in which similar
   organisms live today.

Investigate More!

Research Use the Internet or library resources to identify one of the fossils you examined. Learn where and when the organism lived and any other interesting facts about it. Present your information to the class.

Use with page A117

Name _____ Date _____

Out on a Limb

Procedure

1. **Collaborate** In small groups of 2 or 3 students, examine pictures of the forelimbs of four different animals, such as a cat, lizard, bird, and chimpanzee.

2. **Collaborate** Discuss the forelimbs with a partner. Talk about how alike and different they are. Also discuss how each animal uses its forelimbs.

3. **Record Data** Draw a rough sketch of each forelimb in the space below. Try to show as many bones as you can in your drawings.

4. **Compare** Circle bones that are similar from one drawing to the next.

5. **Research** Find out what the names of the bones are, and label them.

Conclusion

Write the answers to the questions below.

1. **Compare** How are the structures of the forelimbs of these animals similar? How are they different?

   All have a similar arrangement of bones. However, the sizes

   and shapes of these bones differ. Some are covered with

   fur, while others are covered with scales or feathers.

2. **Analyze Data** Did similar bones appear in more than one animal?

   All the forelimbs have metacarpals, carpals, phalanges, and

   a radius and ulna.

3. **Analyze Data** Are there any bones that did not appear in all four animals?

   The numbers of certain bones may differ among the species.

4. **Infer** How do the similarities and differences among these bones suggest that evolution occurred?

   The similarities imply that all these animals evolved from a

   common ancestor.

Investigate More!

Use Models Using colored modeling clay, create a model of two of the forelimbs that you studied. Be sure to model similar structures in the same color.

Use with page A127

You're in the Cycle!

Procedure

1. **Collaborate** Put on safety goggles and keep them on until the end of the activity. Work with a partner. Fill each beaker about half full with water. Use the chart below to record your observations. **Safety:** Do not use the straw to taste or drink water. Only blow out through the straw.

Color of BTB Solution			
Cup	**Color at Start**	**Prediction**	**Color at End**
Experimental Cup	blue		
Control Cup	blue		

2. **Measure** Add the same amount of bromothymol blue (BTB) to both beakers one drop at a time until the water turns blue. BTB is an indicator that changes color in the presence of carbon dioxide.

3. **Predict** What do you think will happen if you blow through a straw into the BTB solution? Record your prediction in your chart. Then, use the straw to carefully blow into the BTB solution in one of the beakers.

4. **Observe** The beaker you blew in is the experimental beaker. The other beaker is the control beaker. Compare the color of the solution in the two beakers.

5. **Record Data** Record your observations in your chart.

Conclusion

Write the answers to the questions below.

1. **Infer** What do your observations tell you about the air you exhale?

   Exhaled air contains carbon dioxide.

   _____

2. **Hypothesize** Do people affect the amount of carbon dioxide added to the atmosphere? How so?

   Yes, more people exhaling puts more carbon dioxide into

   the atmosphere.

   _____

Investigate More!

Design an Experiment Does exercise affect the amount of carbon dioxide in your breath? Design an experiment to find out. Begin by adding the same number of drops to both beakers until the water in both beakers is blue.

Use with page B5

Bag It!

Procedure

1. **Collaborate** Work in a small group. Record your observations in the chart below.

Plant Leaf	Prediction	Observation
Leaf in bag		
Leaf not in bag		

2. **Collaborate** Put a plastic bag over one of the plant's leaves. Take special care not to damage the leaf. Tie the bag closed with a twist tie. The whole leaf should fit inside the bag, and the twist tie should not be too tight. Water the plant and place it near a sunny window.

3. **Predict** What do you think you will find when you check the leaves after two days?

_____

_____

4. **Observe** After two days, observe the plant's leaves and the plastic bag. Note any changes.

_____

_____

5. **Record Data** Record your observations in your chart.

Conclusion

Write the answers to the questions below.

1. **Analyze Data** Look at the observations you recorded. What do your observations tell you about plant leaves and water?

   Plant leaves give off water.

   _____

   _____

2. **Hypothesize** What happened to the water given off by the leaves that were not in a plastic bag?

   It evaporated into the air.

   _____

   _____

Investigate More!

Design an Experiment Find out how sunlight affects water given off by plant leaves. Repeat the activity using two identical plants. Put one plant in a sunny window and the other in a place that stays dark. Observe and compare the leaves after two days.

Use with page B13

Identify Your Food

Procedure

1. **Collaborate** Work in small groups to come up with a list of foods you might eat in one day. Record your list in the chart below.

Food	Some of Ingredients	Source of Energy	Source of Energy	Source of Energy

2. **Record Data** Brainstorm some of the ingredients for each food and record them in your chart. Record each ingredient in a separate row.

3. **Record Data** Try to identify the source of energy for each ingredient. If that energy source also relied on a source of energy, record it in your chart.

4. **Use Models** In the space below, create a food web by drawing a diagram to show the connections of your food sources. Start with yourself at the top. Draw lines to the ingredients in the foods you eat and from them to their sources of energy.

5. **Use Models** Circle the Sun with yellow, organisms that use the Sun as their source of energy with green, and organisms that eat them with red.

Conclusion

Write the answers to the questions below.

1. **Use Models** Based on your model, what do you know about how energy moves through the biosphere?

   Sample answer: Energy moves through the biosphere as

   plants use energy from the Sun and animals eat plants or

   other animals.

2. **Infer** Based on your model, what is the original energy source for all your food?

   the Sun

Investigate More!

Ask Questions What other questions do you have about food sources or food webs? Find the answers to your questions by using library or Internet resources. Communicate what you learn to your class.

Studying Your Biome

Procedure

1. **Record Data** Research to find out the total precipitation and average temperature for each month of the last year in your region. Record your data in the chart below.

Month	Total Precipitation	Average Precipitation
January		
February		
March		
April		
May		
June		
July		
August		
September		
October		
November		
December		

2. **Use Numbers** On graph paper, use a pencil to draw a graph with axes like those on page B38 and B39.

3. **Record Data** For each month, find the temperature that is recorded in your table on the temperature scale of the graph. Use a red pencil to mark the point. Then draw a smooth line through the points.

Use with page B37

4. **Use Numbers** For each month, find the amount of precipitation that is recorded in your table on the precipitation scale of the graph. Use a blue pencil to mark the point. Fill in a blue bar for each month up to its precipitation point.

Conclusion

Write the answers to the questions below.

1. **Analyze Data** Describe the patterns of temperature and precipitation on your graph.

   Answers should describe the general patterns for your area.

   _____

2. **Infer** Compare your climate graph to those on pages B38 and B39. Is the pattern on your climate graph similar to either of those climate graphs? What do you think this means?

   If student's climate graphs are similar to one of those in the

   text, then student lives in that biome.

   _____

Investigate More!

Research Create another climate graph for a different area. It could be somewhere you have been or just a place you find interesting.

An Owl's Dinner

Procedure

1. **Predict** In this activity, you will study the contents of an owl pellet. An owl pellet is a ball of material that an owl coughs up after it has digested a meal. It contains material that the owl's stomach could not digest. Predict what you think an owl pellet contains. Record your prediction on the lines below.

_____

_____

2. **Observe** Use forceps and a large wooden skewer to carefully pull the pellet apart. Use the hand lens to look at the materials in the pellet. Look for fur, feathers, and bones. Then try to separate the materials into groups based on the species of animals they came from.

_____

_____

3. **Measure** Use the metric ruler to measure the lengths of the skulls. Also observe other features of the skulls, such as the number of teeth.

_____

_____

4. **Record Data** Record the skull lengths and other observations on the lines below.

_____

_____

_____

_____

Name _____ Date _____

5. **Classify** Use the drawings in your book to identify as many of the skulls as possible. Record your findings on the lines below. Once you have completed the activity, wash your hands thoroughly with soap and warm water.

_____

_____

_____

_____

Conclusion

Write the answers to the questions below.

1. **Infer** What did the owl eat? Explain how you inferred the answer.

   Based on observation of the bones, the owl ate one or more

   small animals.

2. **Draw Conclusions** What do you know about an owl's role in its ecosystem?

   An owl is a predator (carnivore).

Investigate More!

Design an Experiment Look at the bones other than skulls and jaws. Sort them into different types based on shape and size. Compare the bones and describe their purposes.

Body Color and Survival

Procedure

1. **Collaborate** Work in a small group.

2. **Record Data** Use the chart below to record your observations.

Hunt	Blue	Yellow	Green	Red
Hunt 1				
Hunt 2				
Hunt 3				
Total				

3. **Predict** Use the hole punch to punch 50 circles from each of the sheets of colored paper. The circles represent insects. Predict the color of insect that you think would be hardest for a bird to see against a yellowish sand background. Record your prediction on the lines below.

_____

_____

4. **Use Models** Lay the cloth out flat on the floor. The cloth represents a yellow beach. Scatter the circles randomly on the cloth. Kneel at the edge of the cloth. When your teacher says "go," pick up as many circles as you can, one at a time. Stop 15 seconds later.

5. **Record Data** Add the number of circles of each color that your entire group collected. Record your data in the row marked "Hunt 1." Set aside the insects you picked up. Then repeat step 4 two more times for Hunts 2 and 3.

Use with page B57

Conclusion

Write the answers to the questions below.

1. **Analyze Data** Total the columns. What color had the least number of insects collected? Did this result match your prediction?

   Sample answer: Yellow had the least number of insects

   collected, which matched my prediction.

   _____

2. **Infer** How were the results of each hunt different? Why did this happen?

   Sample answer: More and more yellow dots were collected

   as the dots of other colors grew scarce.

   _____

Investigate More!

Design an Experiment Try the experiment again using a green cloth to represent grass. Compare the results of the two experiments. Explain the results in terms of adaptations of organisms to their environments.

Game of Numbers

Procedure

On Island A, snakes feed on mice, small birds, and other small animals. The data table below shows the populations of snakes and mice over a span of 10 years.

Year	Mice	Snakes
1	850	62
2	810	68
3	720	70
4	600	55
5	340	40
6	450	22
7	580	35
8	700	50
9	250	12
10	260	12

1. **Record Data** On separate sheets of paper, plot the data into two line graphs: one for the mouse population, another for the snake population. Be sure to choose useful scales for each population. The scales do not need to be the same.

2. **Analyze Data** Place the two graphs next to each other, and compare them. Do you see any patterns in the mouse population that repeat in the snake population?

Conclusion

Write the answers to the questions below.

1. **Communicate** Describe the patterns of growth of both the mouse and snake populations. When did each increase? When did each decrease?

   _____

   _____

   _____

2. **Use Numbers** During which year did each population experience the greatest drop? Calculate the percent drop by dividing the decrease by the previous year's population.

   _____

   _____

3. **Infer** What might have caused the population changes that the data indicate? Describe an event that the data would support.

   _____

   _____

   _____

4. **Ask Questions** What further information about Island A would help you better understand the data?

   _____

   _____

Investigate More

Research Find out more about animal populations on islands, such as Hawaii, Guam, and the Galapagos Islands. What factors influence how these populations grow or decline?

Disaster Recovery

Ashfall from a volcanic eruption blankets a community with a meter of ash. Luckily, the entire population evacuated safely before the eruption. Now the returning citizens are faced with a huge ash-covered problem.

Procedure

1. **Collaborate** How can the citizens rebuild their community? Work with a group of three other students to solve this problem. Record your group's ideas here.

   Answers will vary. Groups should consider the size of the

   community and the main problems faced by the citizens.

   _____

   _____

   _____

2. **Communicate** Brainstorm the steps necessary to get the community running again. Consider cleanup, reconstruction, restarting schools and businesses, getting electricity back on, finding funds, and so on. Describe the order in which everything must be done.

   _____

   _____

   _____

   _____

   _____

   _____

   _____

   _____

3. **Classify** Determine whether each project will require government assistance and funding or private assistance and funding. Assign each project to the correct individual, group, or agency.

_____

_____

_____

Conclusion

Write the answers to the questions below.

1. **Communicate** On a separate sheet of paper, create a flow chart to display the steps that will restore the community. Branch the chart to divide public and private projects. Decide who is responsible for completing each task. Charts should present a logical series of steps for recovery that covers the entire community.

2. **Communicate** Beneath your flow chart, write a brief article for the local newspaper that explains the plan to residents. Articles should include a clear explanation of why each step in the plan is necessary.

Investigate More!

Solve a Problem Research to learn how a community rebuilt after the 1980 eruption of Mount St. Helens in Washington. Hold a mock community meeting discussing your plan. Answer questions about it from "residents."

Scratch It!

Procedure

1. **Collaborate** Geologists use the Mohs scale to rate the hardness of minerals. Work in a small group. Arrange the minerals in the Mohs scale in order from 1 to 7. Label the unknown minerals *A*, *B*, and *C*. Record your observations in the chart below.

Mohs Scale	Mineral A	Mineral B	Mineral C
1. Talc			
2. Gypsum			
3. Calcite			
4. Fluorite			
5. Apatite			
6. Feldspar			
7. Quartz			
Hardness of unknown mineral			

2. **Observe** Pressing down hard, scratch mineral A against the talc. Rub any mark left. If the mark rubs off, it is not a real scratch.

3. **Record Data** If mineral A leaves a scratch on the talc, make an X in the row marked Talc. Repeat steps 2 and 3 for the next six minerals in the Mohs scale.

4. **Use Numbers** The hardness of mineral A is between the highest-numbered mineral that it scratched and the lowest-numbered mineral that it did not scratch. Write the estimated hardness of mineral A in the chart.

5. Record Data Repeat steps 2 to 4 for mineral B and mineral C.

Conclusion

Write the answers to the questions below.

1. **Use Numbers** Order the unknown minerals from softest to hardest.

   unknown mineral C, unknown mineral A, unknown

   mineral B

2. **Predict** Based on your data, predict what would happen if you scratched mineral A with mineral B.

   Mineral B would leave a scratch on mineral A, because a

   harder mineral will scratch a softer mineral.

Investigate More!

Design an Experiment Instead of carrying a set of minerals, geologists often use common objects to perform scratch tests. Using the sample materials, test the hardness of your fingernail, a penny, a key, or other common objects.

Use with page C5

Name _____ Date _____

Name That Rock!

Procedure

1. **Collaborate** All rocks can be grouped into three classes—
igneous, metamorphic, and sedimentary. Work in small groups.
Use the chart below to record your observations.

Rock Sample	Rock Name	Rock Class
1		
2		
3		
4		
5		
6		
7		

2. **Observe** Take the first rock sample. Using the hand lens, look
closely at the rock to determine whether it is made of small
grains.

3. **Compare** Follow the steps of the Rock Identification Key to
classify the rock.

4. **Record Data** When you have identified the rock, write its name
and class in your chart.

5. **Observe** Repeat steps 2 and 3 for each remaining rock sample.

Use with page C15

Conclusion

Write the answers to the questions below.

1. **Hypothesize** Geologists group rocks into three classes based on how they are formed. Using your results, hypothesize about how the sandstone might have formed.

   Sandstone appears to be made from compacted sand.

   _____

   _____

2. **Compare** Using your hand lens, look again at the granite, basalt, and sandstone. Note the shape of the grains in each sample. How does the shape of the grains in the igneous rocks differ from the shape of grains in the sedimentary rock?

   The grains in the sedimentary rock are round. In igneous

   rocks, the grains have flat edges that fit together.

   _____

Investigate More!

Design an Experiment Make a plan to gather rocks in nature and investigate their properties. Be sure to have your teacher approve your plan before you carry it out!

Use with page C15

Be a Time Traveler!

Procedure

1. **Collaborate** Work in a small group. Gather your fossil samples and a hand lens. Record your observations in the chart below.
   Observations will vary depending upon the fossil used.

	Fossil A	Fossil B	Fossil C
Shape			
Size			
Other details			
Name of organism			

2. **Observe** Look closely at Fossil A. Use the hand lens to see more detail.

3. **Record Data** Record your observations about Fossil A in your chart. Include its shape, size, and other visible details.

4. **Infer** Using your observations of Fossil A and what you already know about fossils, decide which modern organism the fossil most closely resembles. Write the name of that organism in your chart.

5. **Observe** Repeat steps 2 to 4 for Fossils B and C.

Conclusion

Write the answers to the questions below.

1. **Classify** Classify each fossil as a plant or an animal. Describe the evidence that supports your classification.

   Evidence might include skeletal remains or imprints that

   would indicate an animal fossil, or imprints of leaves that

   would indicate a plant fossil.

   _____

2. **Infer** Based on what you know about organisms that resemble the fossils, what additional information can you infer about the organism that left the fossil?

   Students may be able to infer where the fossil lived, its size

   and shape, and how it obtained energy.

   _____

Investigate More!

Research What types of fossils are found in your state or region? Contact an expert at a local science museum or university or visit Internet sites. Find out what these fossils reveal about changes on Earth.

Use with page C33

Name _____ Date _____

Model Pangaea!

Procedure

1. **Observe** Look at the shapes of the continents on the world map. Based on their shapes, describe how they might have once fit together as a supercontinent called Pangaea.

   Students should suggest that the coastlines of

   South America and Africa once were joined.

2. **Use Models** Trace the shapes of all of the continents onto the tracing paper. Glue the tracing paper to the construction paper. Cut out the continents.

3. **Hypothesize** Try to fit your continents together to form a supercontinent. Sketch your supercontinent in the space below. When you have fit all the continents together, check the map of Pangaea on page C44 to see how closely your supercontinent matches with scientists' reconstruction of Pangaea.

4. **Predict** Based on how the continents fit together in Pangaea, predict the locations where you would expect to find similar rock types and fossils.

   Similar rock types and fossils would most likely be found in

   areas that had similar climates or environments when the

   fossils were formed. So, similar rock types and fossils might

   be found along the coastlines of South America and Africa.

Conclusion

Write the answers to the questions below.

1. **Use Models** Using your model, rearrange the continents in a different way. How might the world look today if the continents were in these positions?

   Answers will vary, but should indicate some understanding

   of how geographic location affects climate and other

   environmental conditions.

2. **Infer** Based on its locations in Pangaea and in the modern world, explain how the climate of North America might have changed from 200 million years ago to the present.

   Most of what is now North America was located in equatorial

   regions when it was part of Pangaea. Therefore, the climate

   probably was once much warmer and has cooled as the

   continent moved north over the last 200 million years.

Investigate More!

Be an Inventor Globes are more accurate than flat maps. Using everyday materials, invent a spherical model of continental drift. How is your model useful? How is it not useful?

Use with page C43

Shake It!

Procedure

1. **Collaborate** Work with a partner. Measure the largest face of each wood block. Cut the sandpaper to fit that face and wrap it around the sides of the block.

2. **Use Models** Large earthquakes are common in regions where plates slide past each other. You can use wood blocks to represent tectonic plates. Practice sliding the two wood blocks past each other. Use the smooth faces of the blocks.

3. **Hypothesize** Discuss with your partner how you think the presence of the sandpaper on the blocks will change the way they slide past each other. Record your hypothesis on the lines below.

Sample answer: I hypothesize that it will be more difficult

to slide the blocks past each other when they have

sandpaper on them.

4. **Use Models** Try sliding the blocks past each other again, this time using the sandpaper faces. Apply pressure to squeeze the plates together while you move them past each other. Record your observations on the lines below.

_____

_____

_____

Conclusion

Write the answers to the questions below.

1. **Analyze Data** Explain how sandpaper-covered blocks better represent the action at plate boundaries than would smooth blocks.

   Plates do not have smooth boundaries. They are made of

   rock that breaks apart in jagged ways.

   _____

2. **Communicate** Using your model, explain how you think earthquakes are caused when pressure builds up at the edges of moving plates.

   Answers will vary, but should demonstrate a general

   understanding of the concept of what happens at

   plate boundaries.

   _____

Investigate More!

Design an Experiment What other questions do you have about earthquakes that can be addressed by using your model? Try using different materials on the faces of the plates to model different rock types that occur at plate boundaries.

Use with page C51

3... 2... 1... Oil Game Over?

Procedure

1. **Collaborate** Work with a partner. Study the chart below of the world's remaining oil reserves. You may organize all or some of the data on a bar graph on a separate sheet of paper.

Country	Proven Reserves (billion barrels)
Saudi Arabia	262
Iraq	112
United Arab Emirates	98
Kuwait	96
Iran	90
Venezuela	78
Russia	49
Libya	29
Mexico	28
China	24
Nigeria	24
United States	23
Qatar	15
Rest of World	106

2. **Use Numbers** Add the amounts of oil in all of the world's proven reserves. Record your total on the line below.

Approximately 1,034 billion barrels

3. **Use Numbers** In 2003, the world used an estimated 80 million barrels of oil per day. Calculate an estimate of how many millions of barrels were used that year.

80 million × 365 days = 29,200 million. The world used about 29,200 million barrels of oil in 2003.

Use with page C67

4. **Predict** Based on your data, calculate an estimate of how long Earth's oil reserves will last at the rate people are using them.

1,034 billion ÷ 29,200 million/year = about 35 years

Conclusion

Write the answers to the questions below.

1. **Use Numbers** The United States uses one-quarter of the world's oil, but has only five percent of the world's population. About how many millions of barrels of oil does the United States use each day?

80 million × 0.25 = 20 million. The United States uses about 20 million barrels of oil each day.

2. **Predict** Over time, countries around the world continue to develop. More people begin to use modern technology, such as appliances and cars. How should you revise your estimate of how long the world's oil reserves will last?

The estimate of how long the oil reserves will last should be lower based on the fact that countries continue to develop and populations continue to increase.

3. **Hypothesize** How can people extend Earth's supply of oil and other fossil fuels?

People can conserve their use of oil and find new sources of energy.

Investigate More!

Solve a Problem Find out how fossil fuels are used in your home, school, and community. Research ways you and your classmates can reduce the use of fossil fuels.

Power It with Sunlight!

Procedure

1. **Collaborate** Work in a small group. Examine the solar panel and the motor. Find the wires that will connect the panel to the motor.

2. **Use Models** Connect one wire from the solar panel to one of the contacts on the motor. Connect the other wire from the solar panel to the other contact on the motor. Hold the motor so that the fan can rotate freely, or mount the motor on a piece of cardboard or wood.

3. **Observe** Place the solar panel in direct sunlight or under a bright lamp. Observe the fan. Then move the panel out of the light. Record your observations on the lines below.

The fan moved when the solar panal was in the light and

stopped moving when the solar panal was removed from

the light.

_____

Conclusion

Write the answers to the questions below.

1. **Infer** Using your knowledge of electricity, propose an explanation for your observations of the solar panel, the wires, and the fan.

The solar panel uses light to produce electricity. The current

travels in a loop through the wires and powers the fan.

_____

_____

2. **Compare** How is the solar panel similar to a battery? How is it different?

Like a battery, the solar panel must be connected to wires

and the motor to create a complete circuit. The solar cell

gets its energy from light. The battery gets its energy

from chemicals inside it. Unlike the solar panel, though,

eventually the chemicals in the battery will be exhausted

and the battery will not work.

_____

3. **Use Models** Create a series circuit by connecting two or more solar panels to the motor. Place the panels in the light and observe the motion of the fan. Compare the motion of the fan using one solar panel to the motion using more solar panels.

The motor will spin faster with more power from more

panels.

Investigate More!

Be an Inventor Using a solar panel and a motor, design and test your own solar-powered invention. You may use other objects, such as empty cans, bottles, straws, rubber bands, or wheels. Present it to the class.

Use with page C79

Warming Up!

Procedure

1. **Collaborate** Work with a partner. Fill one container half full with soil and the other half full with water. Use the chart below to record your observations.

Time (minutes)	Soil Temp. (°C)	Water Temp. (°C)
0		
30		
60		

2. **Measure** Use one thermometer to measure the temperature of the soil and the other thermometer to measure the temperature of the water. Record the data in your chart.

3. **Record Data** Place the two containers in a sunny location. After 30 minutes, measure the temperature in each container and record the data in your chart.

4. **Record Data** After 60 minutes, measure the temperature in each container again and record the data in your chart.

5. **Use Numbers** Calculate the change, if any, in the temperature of the soil between the start and end of this activity. Repeat for the temperature of the water. Record your calculations on the lines below.

_____

_____

_____

_____

Use with page D5

Name _____ Date _____

D.11.1
Investigate Record

Conclusion

Write the answers to the questions below.

1. **Communicate** In the space below, make line graphs showing the temperatures you recorded for the soil and for the water in your chart.

Graphs should show soil temperature rising faster than water temperature. They should have a title and labeled axes.

2. **Infer** Based on the results of your experiment, which do you think heats up faster, land or the ocean?

land

Investigate More!

Design an Experiment Plan a second part to the experiment you just did. Write a procedure to test how quickly different earth materials cool off at night. Try it and graph your results.

Student Resources

54

Copyright © Houghton Mifflin Company. All rights reserved.

Use with page D5

Name _____ Date _____

Spin It!

Procedure

1. **Collaborate** Work with a partner and gather the materials.

2. **Use Models** Push a nail through the center of the cardboard circle. The nail represents the North Pole. The cardboard circle represents Earth from space. The circle should be able to spin easily.

3. **Use Models** Rotate the cardboard circle slowly in a counterclockwise direction. You would see Earth spinning in this direction if you were in space looking down at the North Pole. While you rotate the cardboard, your partner will use a pencil to try to quickly draw a straight line from the center of the circle to the edge.

4. **Record Data** In the space below, draw a diagram showing the line's appearance.

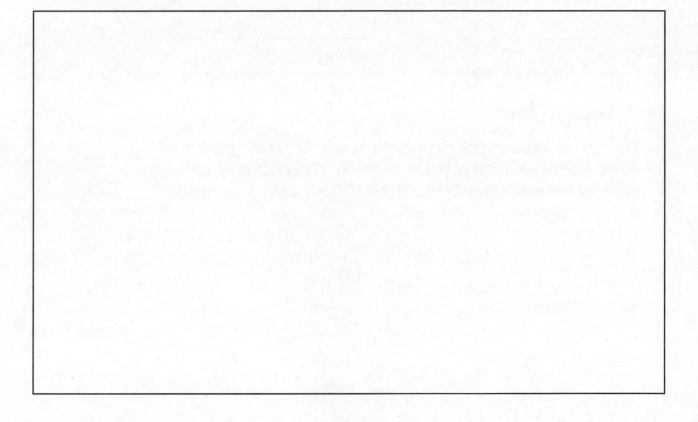

Name _____ Date _____

Conclusion

Write the answers to the questions below.

1. **Analyze Data** In what direction is the line deflected or curved?

   to the left

   _____

2. **Infer** How do you think the deflection of the line relates to how Earth's rotation affects winds and ocean currents?

   Winds and currents do not move in straight lines, because

   of Earth's rotation.

   _____

3. **Express Ideas** Sailors used patterns in Earth's winds long before scientists explained them. Why do you think such patterns were difficult to understand?

   Local effects often affect wind direction, disguising the

   pattern.

   _____

Investigate More!

Design an Experiment Repeat the activity by rotating the cardboard circle in the opposite direction. This illustrates the deflection in the Southern Hemisphere. Draw a diagram showing the line's deflection.

Name _____ Date _____

Being a Weather Forecaster

Procedure

1. **Collaborate** Work with a partner to record weather observations. Record your observations in the chart below.

	Temperature	Cloud Cover and Type	Wind Speed and Direction	Barometric Pressure
Day 1				
Day 2				
Day 3				
Day 4				
Day 5				
Prediction for Day 6				
Actual for Day 6				

2. **Record Data** Each day for five days, make meteorological observations at the same time each day. Record the temperature, cloud cover, and type. If you have the correct instruments, also record wind speed, wind direction, and barometric pressure.

3. **Analyze Data** After collecting data for five days, look for any patterns in your data.

4. **Predict** Based on your analysis of the data, make a prediction about what the weather will be like at the same time tomorrow. Record your prediction in your chart.

5. **Record Data** During the next week, record the same observations as you did in step 2.

Use with page D29

Conclusion

Write the answers to the questions below.

1. **Compare** How accurate was your prediction about what the weather would be like?

   Answers will vary. Students should compare each variable

   when answering the question.

   _____

2. **Infer** Based on the data you continue to collect, can you predict what the weather will be like next week? Why or why not?

   The weather is difficult to predict accurately beyond two or

   three days.

Investigate More!

Design an Experiment Check the local weather forecast and keep records on what the weather is the next day. How does the accuracy of the weather forecasters compare to your weather predictions?

Make a Sundial

Procedure

1. **Measure** Work with a partner. Use an atlas to find the latitude of your location. On cardstock, use the protractor to draw and label an angle equal to your latitude. Make the sides of the angle 6 cm long. **Safety:** Exercise caution when using scissors.

2. **Collaborate** Cut along the angle line to form a triangle. This will be your gnomon (NOH mahn), or sundial stick. Fold the gnomon to make it stand up straight. Cut out a wedge from the vertical side.

3. **Collaborate** Cut a slit in the paper plate and slide in the gnomon. Tape it underneath so that the wedged edge aligns with the plate's inner circle.

4. **Observe** Place the sundial outdoors in a sunny spot. Align the gnomon so it points north. Tape down the sundial. Mark where the straight side of the gnomon's shadow crosses the circle and record the time.

5. **Record Data** Each hour on the hour, mark and label the gnomon's shadow.

Conclusion

Write the answers to the questions below.

1. **Analyze Data** Observe your sundial. What pattern(s) do you see in your time markings?

   The hour markings are closer together near the gnomon.

   _____

2. Use Numbers Take your sundial outside at a time other than on the hour. Point the gnomon north. Observe the shadow and read the sundial to estimate the time. Compare its time to the actual time. How accurate is your sundial?

The sundial will not be as accurate as a clock or watch.

_____

_____

Investigate More!

Design an Experiment Record the date on your sundial. Repeat the activity at different times during the year, using a different color pen to record the data. Look for changes in your data and for possible causes.

Use with page D45

Lights Out

Procedure

1. **Collaborate** Work with a partner. Label the 2 cm ball *Moon* and the 5 cm ball *Earth*. Insert a toothpick into each ball.

2. **Use Models** Insert the toothpicks of the Earth and Moon balls into the foam core about 3 cm apart. Shine a flashlight so that the Moon is between the "Sun" and Earth. Darken the room, then adjust the positions of the Sun or Moon until the Moon's shadow falls onto Earth.

3. **Experiment** The Moon casts a dark shadow and a lighter outer one. The darker shadow creates a total solar eclipse and the lighter shadow creates a partial solar eclipse. Vary the positions of the Moon, Sun, and Earth to model a total solar eclipse, a partial solar eclipse, and no eclipse.

4. **Record Data** Record your results from step 3 in the chart below.

Type of Solar Eclipse	Sketch of Position of Sun, Moon, and Earth	Sketch of Moon's Shadow on Earth
No Eclipse		
Partial Eclipse		
Total Eclipse		

Use with page D55

Conclusion

Write the answers to the questions below.

1. **Analyze Data** When the Moon is between the Sun and Earth, what determines if a solar eclipse occurs?

   the position of the Moon in its orbit

   _____

   _____

2. **Infer** How can total and partial solar eclipses occur at the same time?

   Depending on where two people are on Earth, they may

   simultaneously see a partial eclipse and a total eclipse.

   _____

Investigate More!

Design an Experiment Conduct online research to learn about another type of eclipse—an annular solar eclipse. Write a report that includes diagrams to explain what you learned.

Turning the Tide

Procedure

1. **Collaborate** Work with a partner. Record your observations in the chart below.

	Photograph 1	**Photograph 2**
Difference		
Cause		
Effects		

2. **Use Models** Study the two photographs on page D63 of your book. In the chart, jot down as many specific differences between the photographs as you can.

3. **Use Models** With your partner, discuss the following questions. Record your answers in your chart.

   - What differences do you see in these two photographs of the same stretch of beach at different times?

   - What do you think is the cause of these changes?

   - What effects do you think these changes could have on the beach and on organisms that live there?

Conclusion

Write the answers to the questions below.

1. **Communicate** Write a paragraph explaining the process that is occurring on the beach.

   The tides move back and forth between high tide and low

   tide, gradually covering or exposing the beach.

   _____

   _____

   _____

2. **Hypothesize** What are likely to be the effects of these changes on the beach?

   It gets hot when dry, cool when wet. The sand moves

   somewhat and smoothes out.

3. **Hypothesize** What types of organisms can live in this changing environment?

   They must be able to dig down into the sand or enclose

   themselves so they don't dry out or overheat. They have to

   withstand the force of the waves.

Investigate More!

Design an Experiment How could you test the hypotheses you made about how the changes will affect the beach and what types of organisms could live there?

Use with page D63

Name _____ Date _____

Model Fun!

Procedure

1. **Use Numbers** Use the data chart below to make scale paper models of the planets.

Planet	Radius in km	Distance from Sun in AU
Mercury	2,439	0.4
Venus	6,052	0.7
Earth	6,378	1
Mars	3,397	1.5
Jupiter	71,490	5.2
Saturn	60,268	9.5
Uranus	25,559	19.2
Neptune	25,269	30.1
Pluto	1,160	39.5

2. **Calculate** The astronomical unit (AU) is used to measure distances in space. Use the AU value for each planet in converting these distances into measurements you can use.

3. **Calculate** Convert the radius of each planet and the Sun into a size you can model. Convert the km values into distances you can measure.

4. **Measure** Use the compass to draw each planet and the Sun on construction paper. Label each and cut them out. **Safety:** Exercise caution when using scissors. If necessary, tape several pieces of paper together to make your models.

Use with page D75

5. **Use Numbers** Lay the Sun cutout at one end of the hallway. Use the tape measure to plot the positions of the planets using the values you calculated in step 3.

6. **Use Models** Place each planet cutout at its proper distance from the Sun. You now have a model of the solar system.

Conclusion

Write the answers to the questions below.

1. **Observe** Look at the positions of the planets and the Sun. What patterns, if any, do you observe?

   The smaller planets are closer to the Sun. There is a large

   gap between Mars and Jupiter. The larger planets are farther

   from the Sun.

2. **Infer** Based on your answer to question 1, do you think Pluto is a true planet?

   Sample answer: Because of its small size and great

   distance from the Sun, Pluto may not be a true planet.

   _____

Investigate More!

Research Use the Internet to research the newly-discovered planet Sedna. How can you modify your scale to include Sedna?

Name _____ Date _____

Super Star!

Procedure

1. **Record Data** Scientists assign stars absolute brightness and apparent brightness. Apparent brightness is how bright the star looks from Earth. Record your observations.

2. **Collaborate** Work in small groups. Label the two flashlights *A* and *B*. Tape two large sheets of white paper to the classroom wall.

3. **Measure** Use the meter stick to measure a distance of 1 m from the wall. Use masking tape to mark the spot on the floor.

4. **Compare** With a classmate, stand at the 1-m mark, holding flashlights *A* and *B*. Darken the room. Shine the flashlights onto each sheet of paper on the wall. On the lines below, describe the relative brightness of the central parts of the spots cast by the flashlights.

_____

_____

_____

5. **Measure** Have a classmate stand at the 1-m mark and shine the dimmer flashlight onto the wall. Shining the brighter flashlight onto the wall, walk backward until the spots from the two flashlights appear equally bright. Mark and measure your distance from the wall. Record the distance on the line below.

_____

Use with page D87

Conclusion

Write the answers to the questions below.

1. **Communicate** What two factors affect the apparent brightness of a star?

   distance and light power

   _____

2. **Hypothesize** What can you tell about two stars that appear equally bright from Earth?

   They may be equally distant with equal absolute magnitude.

   Or, if one is brighter than the other, the brighter one is

   farther from Earth.

Investigate More!

Design an Experiment Design an experiment to investigate how brightness varies with distance. Use the two flashlights in the activity and a meter stick or tape measure. Display your data in a graph.

A Giant Atom

Procedure

1. **Collaborate** Work in small groups. Use the tape measure to measure a 3.2 m length of string. Tie the ends together to make a loop. Lay the loop of string on the floor to create a circle. Place a sticky note in the middle of the circle.

2. **Use Models** Use a very sharp pencil to make a tiny hole in the center of the sticky note. The string circle represents an atom. The pencil hole in the sticky note represents the nucleus of the atom.

3. **Measure** Use a metric ruler to estimate the diameter of the pencil hole in millimeters. Use the tape measure to estimate the diameter of the atom in millimeters. Record both measurements on the lines below.

   The pencil hole should be about 1 mm in diameter and the

   atom should be about 1,000 mm.

4. **Use Numbers** Write a ratio in fraction form to compare the diameter of the nucleus to the diameter of the atom in your model.

   Sample answer:1 m/1,000 mm

Conclusion

Write the answers to the questions below.

1. **Analyze Data** The diameter of an actual nucleus is about one ten-thousandth ($\frac{1}{10,000}$) of the diameter of an actual atom. Using the scale of your model, what would the diameter of the pencil hole have to be? (**Hint:** Divide the diameter of your model atom by 10,000.)

   Most pencil holes will be about 1 mm, which gives a ratio of

   1/1,000. The diameter of the pencil hole would have to be

   0.1 mm to have 1/10,000 as the ratio.

Use with page E5

2. **Infer** Almost all of an atom's mass is located in its nucleus. What can you infer about the rest of the atom?

It is mostly empty space.

_____

_____

Investigate More!

Design an Experiment Pencil "lead" is mostly carbon. Draw a pencil line on a piece of paper. Use a ruler to measure its width. Research the size of a carbon atom. Then estimate the number of carbon atoms that would fit across your pencil line.

Use with page E5

Penny Bright

Procedure

1. **Observe** Examine an old, tarnished penny. Record your observations of the penny's appearance on the lines below.

   Answers will vary. _____

   _____

   _____

2. **Experiment** Place the penny in the plastic cup. Sprinkle a small amount of salt on the penny. **Safety:** Wear goggles as you perform the rest of the procedure.

3. **Predict** Pour just enough vinegar in the cup to cover the penny. Leave the uncovered penny in a safe place overnight. Predict what will happen to the penny. Record your prediction on the lines below.

   Answers will vary. _____

   _____

   _____

4. **Observe** After 24 hours, examine the penny to see how it has changed. On the lines below, record your observations of the penny's appearance. If possible, record your observations again after a week has gone by.

   Answers will vary. _____

   _____

   _____

Conclusion

Write the answers to the questions below.

1. **Compare** Compare the properties of the penny before and after you let it sit in the salt-and-vinegar solution.

   Properties noted should be physical, such as color, texture,

   and size. Students should note that the copper oxide tarnish

   disappeared or was diminished.

2. **Infer** Older pennies have a coating of copper oxide (CuO) that makes them look darker and duller than a new penny. What can you infer about the effect of the salt-and-vinegar solution on this coating? What can you infer from your observations of the solution with the penny after a week?

   The salt and vinegar solution causes the copper oxide to

   dissolve. The salt and vinegar do not react with the penny

   itself.

Investigate More!

Design an Experiment Test the effects of a salt-and-vinegar solution on a new iron nail. What changes do you notice? What can you infer about the nail and the solution based on your observations?

How Sweet!

Procedure

1. Measure Use a balance to find the mass of a sugar cube. Record the mass on the line below. Then measure and set aside 3 separate amounts of loose sugar, each with the same mass as the sugar cube.

Answers will vary. _____

_____

2. Observe Fill two beakers with 100 mL of water each. Place the sugar cube in one beaker and an equal amount of loose sugar in the other. Observe both beakers after 5 minutes and record your observations on the lines below.

Answers will vary. _____

_____

3. Measure Empty, wash, and dry both beakers. Then fill each with 100 mL of water. Add equal amounts of loose sugar to each beaker. Stir the mixture in one of the beakers rapidly for 30 seconds.

4. Record Data Observe the sugar-water mixture in the two beakers and record your observations on the lines below.

Answers will vary. _____

_____

_____

_____

Use with page E27

Conclusion

Write the answers to the questions below.

1. **Analyze Data** In step 2, how did particle size affect the rate at which the sugar dissolved? In step 4, how did the stirring affect this rate?

   Loose sugar dissolved more quickly than the sugar cube.

   Stirring increased the rate at which it dissolved.

   _____

2. **Hypothesize** How do you think particle size and stirring affects the rate at which sugar dissolves?

   Loose sugar particles have more surface area. This allows

   the water molecules to contact individual sugar particles

   more quickly, increasing the rate of dissolving. Stirring also

   increases the rate of contact between water molecules and

   sugar particles.

   _____

Investigate More!

Design an Experiment Design an experiment to determine how temperature affects the rate at which sugar dissolves in water. List your materials, write your procedure, and identify safety precautions to follow.

Name _____ Date _____

Acid Test

Procedure

1. **Predict** Predict whether each of the following liquids is an
   acid or a base: vinegar, solution of baking soda, lemon juice,
   apple juice, and ammonia solution. Record your predictions
   in the chart below.

Sample	Prediction	Litmus Paper Results
Vinegar		
Baking Soda Solution		
Lemon Juice		
Apple Juice		
Ammonia Solution		

2. **Observe** Using a stirring rod, place one small drop of vinegar
   on a piece of blue litmus paper and one small drop on red litmus
   paper. Observe and record any color changes in your chart.
   Rinse and dry the stirring rod. **Safety:** Do not taste any of the
   liquids. Wear goggles as you perform the procedure.

3. **Observe** Repeat step 2 for the other liquids. Remember to use
   fresh pieces of litmus paper for each liquid.

Conclusion

Write the answers to the questions below.

1. **Classify** Blue litmus paper turns red in the presence of an acid. Red litmus paper turns blue in the presence of a base. Classify each liquid as an acid or a base. Record your conclusions on the lines below.

   Vinegar, lemon juice, and apple juice are acids. Baking soda

   and ammonia are bases.

2. **Infer** Based on your observations, do you think foods that contain acids taste sour or bitter? (Base your answer on your observations of the litmus papers.)

   sour

Investigate More!

Classify Use universal indicator paper to determine the acidity of several foods, common household products, and water.

Name _____ Date _____

Cool the Air

Procedure

1. **Collaborate** Cap an empty plastic bottle and place it in an ice-water bath. After 5 minutes, open the cap and reseal it quickly. Make sure the inside of the bottle stays dry. Allow the bottle to sit in the ice bath for at least 5 minutes longer.

2. **Experiment** Run hot water over a second, uncapped plastic bottle. After 1 minute, cap the bottle. Make sure the inside of the bottle stays dry.

3. **Predict** Read step 4 and predict its outcome. Record your predictions on the lines below.

_____

_____

_____

4. **Observe** Put the warmed bottle in the ice-water bath. Observe any changes in the shape of the bottle. Run hot water over the cooled bottle from step 1. Observe any changes in the shape of the bottle. What happens when you uncap each bottle? Record your observations on the lines below.

_____

_____

_____

_____

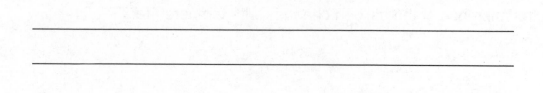

Use with page E49

Conclusion

Write the answers to the questions below.

1. **Analyze Data** Compare the changes in the two bottles.

   The cold bottle bulged outward as it was warmed; the warm

   bottle buckled inward as it cooled. In both instances,

   removing the cap caused a rush of air and caused the

   bottle to return to its original shape.

2. **Compare** Was your prediction correct? Why or why not?

   Answers will vary. Students should accurately report their

   predictions and compare them to the results.

3. **Hypothesize** Why do you think the shapes of the bottles changed in step 4? Propose a hypothesis to explain the changes in the bottles.

   Air expanded inside the warm bottle. When the bottle was

   uncapped, air rushed out until the pressure inside was the

   same as the pressure outside. The opposite happened with

   the cold bottle.

Investigate More!

Design an Experiment Compare the circumference of a blown-up balloon at different temperatures. Make a graph that shows how the circumference of the balloon changes with temperature.

Use with page E49

Name _____ Date _____

Making Change

Procedure

1. **Observe** Fill a small plastic cup $\frac{1}{4}$ full with vinegar. Fill a second plastic cup $\frac{1}{4}$ full with water. Label the cups.

2. **Experiment** Place 2 spoonfuls of baking soda on a paper towel. On the lines below, record your observations about the properties of these three substances.

_____

_____

_____

3. **Predict** Predict what will happen when you combine baking soda with each of the two substances. Record your observations in the chart below.

	Prediction	Observation
Baking soda and water		
Baking soda and vinegar		

4. **Experiment** Place 1 spoonful of baking soda in each cup. Record your observations in your chart.

Use with page E59

Conclusion

Write the answers to the questions below.

1. **Analyze Data** Compare the changes that take place in each cup.

   The baking soda mixes with the water, forming a cloudy

   mixture. The baking soda reacts with the vinegar, forming

   bubbles of gas.

2. **Compare** Were your predictions correct? Why or why not?

   Answers will vary.

3. **Infer** A chemical change differs from a physical change in that one or more new substances are formed in a chemical change. Make an inference to identify which change is a chemical change and which change is a physical change.

   Combining the vinegar and baking soda produces a

   chemical change, because a new substance (a gas) formed.

   The baking soda only dissolved in the water, which is a

   physical change.

Investigate More!

Design an Experiment Use litmus paper to identify whether each substance and each mixture is acidic, basic, or neutral. Experiment with adding different amounts of each substance to determine if you can change the pH.

It's a Gas!

Procedure

1. **Collaborate** With a partner, fill a 1-liter plastic soda bottle $\frac{1}{4}$ full of water. Break 3 effervescent tablets into pieces small enough to fit through the opening of the bottle.

2. **Measure** Place the bottle cap, the broken tablets, and the bottle with the water on a balance. Measure the total mass and record it in the chart below.

	Mass
Separate ingredients	
Combined ingredients, bottle capped	
Combined ingredients, bottle uncapped	

3. **Observe** Put the broken tablets into the bottle and quickly place the cap on tightly. Record your observations on the lines below.

_____

_____

4. **Measure** When the reaction has finished, place the bottle back on the balance. Measure the total mass and record it in your chart.

Use with page E67

5. **Observe** Uncap the bottle. Record your observations on the lines below.

_____

_____

6. **Measure** Place the bottle and cap on the balance again. Measure the total mass and record it in your chart.

Conclusion

Write the answers to the questions below.

1. **Compare** Compare the masses that you recorded. How do they differ?

The masses before and after the reaction are the same.

Uncapping the bottle releases the gas that formed, and the

mass decreases.

2. **Infer** Was matter created or destroyed in this activity? Use your data to support your answer.

The masses before and after the reaction were the same, so

no matter was lost during the reaction. The decreased mass

after the bottle was uncapped was due to gas escaping into

the room, and not because matter was destroyed.

Investigate More!

Design an Experiment What results would you expect if you left the cap off the bottle? Carry out a new experiment to compare the mass of the system before and after the reaction.

Swing Time!

Procedure

1. **Collaborate** Work with a partner. Tie one end of the string to the washer. Tie the other end to one end of the ruler.

2. Place the ruler between the book and the desk so that the end with the string extends off the desk. Make sure the washer can swing freely from side to side.

3. **Compare** Raise the washer to the height of the ruler. Make sure the string is straight. Release the washer. Observe the speed of the washer as it travels through the bottom of its swing. Compare the washer's starting height to the height it reaches on the other side. Record your observations on the lines below.

_____

_____

4. **Compare** Repeat step 2, but this time raise the washer only about one-half as high. Record your observations on the lines below.

_____

_____

5. **Predict** Choose three heights from which to release the washer. Predict from which heights the washer will travel the slowest and the fastest through the bottom of its swing. Test your prediction. Record your prediction and your observations on the lines below.

_____

_____

_____

Conclusion

Write the answers to the questions below.

1. **Communicate** Energy is stored in the washer as you raise it. When you release the washer, some stored energy changes into energy of motion. In the space below, sketch the washer's path as it swings. Label where the stored energy and the energy of motion are greatest.

> Diagrams will vary. Students should see that the washer had the most stored energy when it was being held the highest. It had the most energy of motion at the bottom of the swing.

2. **Hypothesize** Form a hypothesis about the starting height of the washer's swing and its speed at the bottom of the swing.

> The higher the starting point, the faster the washer is moving at the bottom of the swing.

Investigate More!

Design an Experiment Put two rulers side by side and hang washers at the same height. What happens when you raise one washer and then release it, letting it hit the second washer? Record the results of your experiment here.

Make Waves!

Procedure

1. **Collaborate** Work in a group. Use the chart below to record your observations.

Wave Type	Trial	Distance (cm)
Transverse		
Longitudinal		

2. **Experiment** Tie a piece of yarn every 25 cm along the spring. Stretch the spring across the floor, keeping it as near to the floor as possible. Use tape to mark the position of one piece of yarn.

3. **Observe** As your partner holds steady the far end of the spring, shake the other end sideways over a few centimeters. This makes a transverse wave. Mark how far the yarn moved. Measure the distance and record it in your chart.

4. **Record Data** Repeat step 3 for several trials, shaking a bit harder or softer. Record your observations in your chart.

5. **Experiment** Place the meter stick on the floor under the spring. Align the 50-cm mark with one of the pieces of yarn. Tape the meter stick in place.

6. **Observe** Squeeze some coils together, then release them. This makes a longitudinal wave. Measure how far the yarn travels and record it in your chart. Repeat for several trials.

Conclusion

Write the answers to the questions below.

1. **Compare** How are transverse waves and longitudinal waves similar? How are they different? Refer to your observations of the yarn in your answer.

   Both move and then return to a starting position. Transverse

   waves move side to side or up and down. Longitudinal waves

   move forward and backward, or parallel to the direction of

   travel.

2. **Infer** How might waves be used to transmit information?

   Answers will vary.

   _____

   _____

Investigate More!

Be an Inventor Invent a code for sending messages using longitudinal waves. Take turns having two group members transmit a message for the rest of the group to decipher.

Use with page F13

Circling Around!

Procedure

1. **Collaborate** Work in a small group. Use the chart below to record your observations.

Time (minutes)	Temperature Near Ice (°C)	Temperature Near Hot Rock (°C)
0		
1		
2		
3		
4		
5		

2. **Experiment** Add water to the container. Drop the hot rock into one corner of the container. Float the ice cube in the opposite corner.

3. **Observe** When the water is still, add several drops of food coloring next to the ice cube. Observe how the food coloring moves. Record your observations on the lines below.

_____

_____

4. **Measure** Use the thermometer to measure the water temperature near the rock and near the ice cube. Be careful to disturb the water as little as possible. Record the temperature in your chart. Repeat the measurement every minute for 5 minutes.

5. **Communicate** In the space below, draw and label sketches of any currents you observe in the water.

Use with page F23

Conclusion

Write the answers to the questions below.

1. **Communicate** Uneven heating causes a liquid or gas to move in a loop called a convection current. Describe any convection currents you observed.

   The hot water rose and the cool water sank, creating a

   loop.

2. **Infer** How would the currents change if you moved the hot rock or ice cube to new positions? Try it!

   The current would change shape or direction.

3. **Analyze Data** On a separate sheet of paper, make a line graph to show how the water temperatures at each end change with time. How do changes in water temperature affect the convection current?

   Currents move faster as temperature differences become

   greater.

Investigate More!

Research What role does convection play in nature? Research how a lake surface freezes in winter or how a thunderstorm forms.

Use with page F23

Name _____ Date _____

Mix It Up!

Procedure

1. **Collaborate** Work with a partner. Use a compass to draw a circle with a radius of about 5 cm on the white paper. Divide the circle into three equal sectors. Color each part a different color: red, blue, and green. Make a disk by cutting around the circumference of the circle. Use the pushpin to make a hole in the center of the disk.

2. **Predict** On the lines below, write a prediction of what you think you will observe if you spin the disk.

_____

_____

3. **Observe** Unfold one end of the paper clip. Place the disk on the paper clip with the unfolded end through the hole. Spin the disk slowly, then rapidly. Record the appearance of the disk at different rates of spinning.

_____

_____

Conclusion

Write the answers to the questions below.

1. **Communicate** Describe your observations of the disk when it was spinning slowly and when it was spinning rapidly.

As the disk was spinning slowly, each color could be seen.

As the disk began to spin faster, the colors blended into

white.

Use with page F37

2. Compare How is the quickly spinning disk similar to a rainbow? How is it different?

They share some colors. In a rainbow, you can see all of the

colors. In the quickly spinning disk, you can see only white.

_____

3. Infer What might explain the appearance of the disk when it was spinning rapidly?

White light is made of all the colors.

_____

Investigate More!

Design an Experiment Using other disks, find out how different color combinations appear when the disks are spun.

Name _____ Date _____

Let It Shine!

Procedure

1. **Collaborate** Stand facing a partner about 1 m apart. Hold a piece of white cardboard and shine a flashlight on a mirror held by your partner. Position the mirror so that light is reflected onto the cardboard. Record your observations in the chart below.

Material	Behavior of Light

2. **Observe** Shine the flashlight on clear plastic, wax paper, clear colored plastic, black construction paper, and white construction paper. Record your observations in your chart.

3. Look at objects through the prism. Record your observations in your chart.

4. Hold a hand lens between a window or bright light source and a piece of white cardboard. Move the lens toward the cardboard until an image is focused on the cardboard. Record your observations in your chart.

Use with page F49

5. **Record Data** Put a pencil in a cup of water. Look at the pencil from above the cup, and then through the side. Record your observations in your chart.

Conclusion

Write the answers to the questions below.

1. **Analyze Data** Different materials cause light to behave in different ways. Look at the data you recorded. How would you describe some of the ways that light behaves when it interacts with different materials?

    Sample answer: Light bends when it enters water. Light that

    passes through a prism creates a rainbow. Light is reflected

    by white construction paper and is absorbed by black

    construction paper.

2. **Infer** Based on your data, infer whether some materials absorb more light than others. How do your results support your inference?

    Sample answer: Some materials, such as opaque and dark

    materials, absorb more light. Students should use data

    from their table to support this answer.

Investigate More!

Design an Experiment Tape two mirrors together at about a 60° angle. Place the mirrors on a table, and place a small object between the mirrors. How many reflections of the object do you see? Vary the angle between the mirrors and observe what happens.

Use with page F49

Get Wired

Procedure

1. **Collaborate** Work with a partner to assemble the circuit as shown on page F69 of your book.

2. **Record Data** Draw a diagram of the circuit in the space below.

3. **Experiment** Move the switch to position 1. Record your observations in the chart below.

Switch	Observations
Position 1	Students should observe that one bulb is brightly lit.
Position 2	Students should observe that all three bulbs are dimly lit.

4. **Predict** Predict what will happen when you move the switch to position 2. Record your prediction on the lines below.

_____

_____

5. **Use Variables** Move the switch to position 2. Record your observations in your chart. Was your prediction correct?

_____

Use with page F69

Name _____ Date _____

Conclusion
Write the answers to the questions below.

1. **Analyze Data** What difference did it make to move the switch from the second position to the third position?

   All three lights were lit, but they were all dim.

   _____

2. **Infer** What determined the brightness of the bulbs in each step? How was this related to the position of the switch?

   The brightness of the bulbs depended on how they were
   arranged in the circuit and the position of the switch. In
   this circuit, the current had only one path to take. When it
   flowed through three bulbs, each was dimmer than the one
   bulb that was lit in step 2.

Investigate More!

Design an Experiment Where in the circuit would you place a light bulb that would light when the switch was closed in either of the two positions? Draw a diagram on a separate sheet of paper. Test your idea.

Where Is North?

Procedure

1. Place the compass on the table. Wait for the compass needle to come to rest. Connect one end of the wire to the negative terminal of the battery.

2. **Collaborate** Hold the wire above the compass needle and aligned with the needle as shown on page F81 of your book. Have your partner briefly touch the positive battery terminal with the open end of the wire.

3. **Observe** Record your observations on the lines below.

_____

_____

_____

4. **Predict** Predict what will happen if you repeat the experiment with the battery connections reversed. Record your prediction on the lines below.

_____

_____

_____

5. **Observe** Repeat the experiment with the battery connections reversed. Record your observations on the lines below.

_____

_____

_____

Name _____ Date _____

Conclusion

Write the answers to the questions below.

1. **Analyze Data** In step 1, what happened to the compass needle when you disconnected the wire?

   _____

   _____

2. **Compare** Compare your observations from steps 2 and 5. Under what conditions does the compass needle move?

   The needle moves when it is near a wire with current

   running through it.

3. **Hypothesize** How does the current in the wire affect the compass needle? How does this effect compare to that of Earth's magnetic field? Explain.

   The needle rotates when it is near the current, showing

   that the effect of the current is greater than the effect of the

   Earth's magnetic field, because it is so close.

   _____

Investigate More!

Design an Experiment Working with a partner, repeat steps 2 and 5 but with the compass placed above the wire. Record your observations. Compare your results.

Make a Parachute

Procedure

1. **Collaborate** Work with a partner to build a parachute. Cut a 30 cm × 30 cm square from a plastic bag. Cut four 30 cm pieces of string. Tape one end of each piece of string to each corner of the square. Tie the other ends to the metal washer. **Safety:** Be careful with scissors.

2. **Predict** How do you think the parachute will change the way a washer falls? Write your prediction on the lines below.

   _____

   _____

3. **Experiment** Test your prediction. Drop the washer with the parachute and a plain metal washer from the same height above the floor at the same time. Compare how they fall. Record the results on the lines below.

   _____

   _____

4. **Experiment** Perform other trials. With your teacher's permission, drop parachutes and washers from other heights. Measure and record the time they take to fall.

   _____

   _____

Conclusion

Write the answers to the questions below.

1. **Analyze Data** Compare your prediction in step 2 to the results.

   The washer falls more slowly when it has a parachute.

   _____

2. **Hypothesize** Form a hypothesis to explain how a parachute works. Propose an experiment to test this hypothesis.

   A parachute creates resistance to motion through air. To

   test the hypothesis, students could punch small holes in

   the plastic bag. The parachute will fall more quickly.

   _____

3. **Predict** When are parachutes most useful? Describe a situation where a parachute would not be useful to slow someone's rate of falling.

   Parachutes are used to slow falling objects so they hit the

   ground gently. They are not useful very close to the ground.

   _____

Investigate More!

Design an Experiment Will a larger area of plastic change the rate at which a parachute falls? Design and conduct an experiment to find out.

Move a Cube

Procedure

1. **Collaborate** Work with a partner. Record your observations in the chart below.

	Distance Traveled with First Ball	Distance Traveled with Second Ball
Cube only		
Cube with small mass		
Cube with medium mass		
Cube with large mass		

2. Create a ramp by placing 5 textbooks under one end of a board. Place a plastic cube at the bottom of the ramp. Put a piece of tape next to the cube to mark its position (make sure the tape will not interfere with the movement of the cube).

3. **Record Data** Release a ball from the top of the ramp to hit the cube. Measure the distance the cube travels when hit. Record the data in your chart.

4. **Predict** Return the cube to its original position. Tape the 10-g mass to the cube. Predict how far the cube will travel when step 3 is repeated. Record your prediction below.

_____

5. **Experiment** Test your prediction and record the result. Repeat step 3 using the 50-g mass, then the 100-g mass.

6. **Experiment** Repeat the experiment using a ball with greater mass. Record your data.

Conclusion

Write the answers to the questions below.

1. **Analyze Data** How does the motion of an object change with its mass? How does the motion of an object change when the force applied to it changes?

   An object with greater mass does not move as much as an

   object with less mass. When the same force is applied, a

   larger mass moves less. When more force is applied, the

   object moves farther.

2. **Infer** Based on your data, what relationship exists between mass, force, and motion?

   The more mass an object has, the more force it takes to

   move it.

Investigate More!

Design an Experiment Does the type of surface under the cube affect the way it moves when hit? Experiment with wax paper, sandpaper, or other surfaces.

Name _____ Date _____

Lifting , Lifting

Procedure

1. **Collaborate** Work with a partner. Tie a string to a spring scale. Hang a mass from the other end of the string.

2. **Measure** Lift the scale to raise the mass 10 cm above the table. In the space below, record the force shown on the scale, and draw the arrangement next to your numerical data.

3. **Experiment** Arrange a pulley as shown on page F121 of your book. Place the mass from step 1 at one end of the string, and the scale at the other. Lift the mass 10 cm off the table by pulling the spring scale down. Record the force, then draw the arrangement in the space below.

4. Repeat step 3 using two pulleys, as shown in your book. Draw your arrangement and record the force in the space below.

5. Repeat step 3 using four pulleys, as shown in your book. Draw your arrangement and record the force in the space below.

6. Use Variables Investigate other ways to arrange the pulleys and the mass. Measure the force. Draw each arrangement and record the results in the space below.

Conclusion

Write the answers to the questions below.

1. Analyze Data Which arrangement requires the least force to lift the mass a distance of 10 cm?

the four-pulley arrangement

2. Hypothesize How do pulleys change the force needed to lift objects? Form a hypothesis about the way a pulley works.

A pulley makes it easier to lift a load. In a pulley, the load is

divided among the strands of rope; less force is used to lift

something.

Investigate More!

Design an Experiment In each of the three pulley arrangements, what length of string must you pull down to raise a mass 10 cm? Write a new procedure and follow the steps to find out.

Name _____ Date _____

Classify Common Objects

Skill: Compare

Materials

- classroom objects

Procedure

1. **Classify** Observe the classroom objects indicated by your teacher. As a class, discuss how the objects are similar and how they are different. Name several categories into which the objects could be placed.

   Sample answers: things you write with, things made of

   paper

2. **Collaborate** Your teacher will write your suggested categories on the board. As a class, classify each object. Your teacher will list the object under the appropriate heading.

Conclusion

1. **Compare** Name one way that the objects you examined were similar. Name one way that the objects were different.

   Answers will vary depending upon the objects examined.

   Students might note that all of the objects are used in the

   classroom, but that their shapes are different.

2. **Classify** Look at the category with the greatest number of objects. What is one way that those objects could be further classified?

   Sample answer: Objects used for writing could be further

   classified as things that have ink (pens) and things that do

   not (chalk, pencil).

Demonstrate Dichotomy

Skill: Classify

Materials

• pictures of plants

Procedure

1. **Collaborate** Work in groups. Your teacher will give each group a picture of a plant. Observe the characteristics of your plant.

2. **Classify** Look at the dichotomous key your teacher has drawn on the board. Which of the characteristics listed in the key apply to your plant? Which do not apply?

   Sample answers: has seeds/has no seeds, is green, has

   leaves, has needles

3. **Communicate** Could the key you are using help you to identify other plants? How?

   Sample answer: Yes, the characteristics in the key could

   help me classify other plants.

Conclusion

1. **Classify** Collect more examples of plants. Develop a more detailed dichotomous key to classify the plants.

   Keys should have a wider range of traits than those used

   for the first activity. Traits may include color, leaf or petal

   patterns, and surface texture.

2. **Infer** What do you think are some characteristics scientists may use to further classify plants?

   Sample answer: Scientists often use internal characteristics

   and genetic factors, as well as external traits like leaf shape

   and color, to classify plants.

Use with page A15

Name _____ Date _____

Shared Characteristics

Materials

- pictures of various animals

Skill: Communicate

Procedure

1. **Collaborate** Work in groups. Your teacher will give each group some pictures of animals. Observe the pictures.

2. **Classify** List some characteristics you could use to classify the animals into groups.

   Sample answers: has feathers, has teeth, lives in water

3. **Classify** Using the characteristics you recorded above, divide the animals into groups. List the groups here.

   Sample answers: under the heading *Has Feathers*, robin

   and blue jay; under the heading *Has Fur*, mouse and rabbit

4. **Communicate** Share your group's results with the class.

Conclusion

1. **Infer** What characteristics do all animals have in common?

   Answers may include being able to move, being able to eat,

   and having many cells.

2. **Communicate** Make a chart showing how you grouped the animals. Explain why you organized the groups as you did.

   Any logical grouping is acceptable.

   _____

Use with page A27

Name _____ Date _____

Draw a Cell

Skill: Use Models

Materials

- drawing paper
- colored markers

Procedure

1. **Observe** Look at the drawing of a plant cell found on page A47 of your science textbook.

2. **Use Models** Using the paper and markers your teacher has distributed, make your own drawing of a plant cell. Include all of the labeled structures from the diagram in the book.

3. **Collaborate** With the students sitting near you, discuss the function of each of the labeled structures.

Conclusion

1. **Infer** Look at your drawing. Why do you think plants have a thick wall surrounding each cell?

   Thick walls help support the plant cells and the

   plant. Thick walls also protect the plant cells.

2. **Infer** Both plant cells and animal cells have a cell membrane. Think about the function of the cell membrane to explain why it is found in both plant cells and animal cells.

   Sample answer: Both plant and animal cells need to

   control what comes into the cell and what leaves the cell.

   The cell membrane performs this function in both plant and

   animal cells.

Use with page A45

Name _____ Date _____

Inky Diffusion

Materials

- two medium-sized beakers of water
- food coloring

Procedure

1. **Observe** Watch as your teacher adds food coloring to the water in the beaker. Describe your observations immediately after the food coloring is added to the water.

   Answers will vary, but students should observe that the
   food coloring is still localized in one part of the water.

2. **Observe** Record the appearance of the food coloring and the water after 15 minutes.

   Answers will vary, but students should observe that the
   food coloring has spread throughout the water.

Conclusion

1. **Infer** By what process did the food coloring spread throughout the water?

   diffusion

2. **Infer** How did this demonstration model how materials move in and out of cells?

   Materials move in and out of cells by diffusion.

3. **Infer** How was this demonstration *different* from the way materials move into and out of cells?

   Materials moving into or out of a cell pass through a
   membrane. Our demonstration did not model a membrane.

Name _____   Date _____

Bread in a Bag

Skill: Infer

Materials

- slice of bread with no preservatives
- slice of bread with preservatives
- two plastic bags

Safety
• Caution students
not to open the
bags at any point
and to follow
instructions for
proper disposal.

Procedure

1. **Experiment** Place the bread with no preservatives in a plastic bag. Place the bread with preservatives in the other plastic bag. Seal the bags. Place both bags in a warm area. What do you predict will happen?

Answers will vary. Students will probably predict that

more mold will grow on the bread with no preservatives.

2. **Observe** Record the appearance of the bread each day.

Answers
will vary, but
students
should
observe
mold growth
sooner on the
bread with no
preservatives.

	No Preservatives	Preservatives
Day 1		
Day 2		
Day 3		
Day 4		
Day 5		

Conclusion

1. **Infer** What is the function of preservatives in bread?

Preservatives inhibit the growth of mold and bacteria.

2. **Infer** Describe one way that everyday life would be different without food preservatives.

Students may suggest that they would have to bake or buy

bread daily or shop more often.

Vegetative Propagation

Skill: Analyze Data

Materials

• cuttings of spider plant stems taken at different times over several weeks

Procedure

1. **Observe** Observe the cuttings that your teacher has prepared from a spider plant. What differences do you notice between the plants?

   Answers may vary. Students should note that some cuttings

   have grown roots.

2. **Record Data** On a separate sheet of paper, make a drawing of each cutting.

3. **Analyze Data** Why was it necessary for the cuttings to be taken at different times over the past few weeks?

   to have cuttings at different stages

Conclusion

1. **Infer** Is this method a good way for spider plants to reproduce?

   Yes, the plant seems successful.

2. **Predict** Based on your observations, what would happen if you were to leave the spider plant cuttings for several more weeks?

   The cuttings would continue to develop. Some would

   become ready to plant in soil.

Name _____ Date _____

Chromosomes in Motion

Skill: Use Models

Materials

• construction paper

Procedure

1. **Observe** Watch as your teacher sets up circles and strips of construction paper to model the arrangement of chromosomes in sex cells.

2. **Use Models** How can the cells in the model be combined?

   A female and a male sex cell can be combined.

3. **Record Data** In the space below, draw some of the combinations that can be made.

Conclusion

1. **Infer** How does the model your teacher created show the inheritance of traits?

   The model shows how the chromosomes from each sex cell

   are joined into new combinations.

2. **Compare** How does an original female sex cell compare with a newly created cell?

   Half of the information in the newly created cell comes from

   the female sex cell.

Use with page A87

Name _____ Date _____

Take a Look Around

Skill: Classify

Materials

• pencil

Procedure

1. **Collaborate** Your teacher will create a chart on the board. Working together as a class, list some traits (such as eye color, attached earlobes, dimples, or freckles) in the chart and tally how many students in the class have each of the traits.

2. **Record Data** On the lines below, record how many students have each of the traits.

Answers will vary.

_____

_____

_____

_____

Conclusion

1. **Analyze Data** Which traits are most common among the members of your class? Which traits are the least common?

Answers will vary.

_____

_____

_____

2. **Infer** Which traits are dominant? Which traits are recessive?

Answers should reflect that dominant traits include brown

eye color, unattached ear lobes, dimples, and freckles.

Recessive traits include blue eye color, attached ear lobes,

no dimples, and no freckles.

Use with page A101

Name _____ Date _____

Fossilized Shells

Skill: Compare

Materials

• shells   • metric ruler

Procedure

1. **Collaborate** Work with a team. Your teacher will give each team a shell. Use the ruler to measure the shell. Record your measurements and a description of your shell on the lines below.

   Answers will vary.

   _____

2. **Measure** List the different ways you can measure the shell.

   length, width, depth, circumference

3. **Research** What sort of animal may have lived in the shell?

   Answers will vary.

Conclusion

1. **Infer** Why did the shell last longer than the animal that lived inside?

   The shell is much harder.

2. **Compare** Based on your observations, if you were to press the shell and the animal into soft clay, which would make a deeper impression? Why?

   The shell would make a deeper impression because it is

   harder.

Use with page A117

Similar Limbs

Skill: Infer

Materials

- pencil

Procedure

1. **Collaborate** Work together with your classmates to create a list on the board of animals that can stretch out their paws. Compare the body structures of each of these animals to those of humans.

2. **Compare** How does the body structure of a cat compare to that of a dog?

   similar body structure, different size
   _____

   _____

3. **Compare** What other similarities are there between the organisms listed?

   Answers will vary.
   _____

   _____

   _____

Conclusion

1. **Analyze Data** Compare the upper limbs, lower limbs, and other body structures of the animals you listed.

   Answers will vary.
   _____

   _____

2. **Infer** Based on your observations, which two species, of the ones listed, are most closely related? Explain your answer.

   Answers will vary.
   _____

   _____

Use with page A127

Name _____ Date _____

CO$_2$ in the H$_2$O

Skill: Predict

Materials

- beaker
- water
- bromothymol blue
- straw
- safety goggles

Procedure

1. **Observe** Your teacher has added bromothymol blue to a beaker of water. Bromothymol blue changes color when carbon dioxide is present. Observe the beaker of water.

2. **Predict** What do you think will happen when your teacher uses a straw to blow air into the glass?

   Answers will vary. Most students should predict

   that the color will change.

3. **Record Data** What happened when air was blown into the water?

   The water turned clear.

Conclusion

1. **Infer** What do your observations tell you about the air you exhale?

   Exhaled air contains carbon dioxide.

2. **Hypothesize** Do people affect the amount of carbon dioxide added to the atmosphere? How so?

   Yes, more people exhaling puts more carbon

   dioxide into the atmosphere.

Making Rain

Skill: Infer

Materials

- clear bowl
- aluminum pie plate
- hot water
- ice cubes

Procedure

1. **Prepare** Fill the clear bowl with hot water. Use caution when handling the hot water.

2. **Observe** Fill the pie plate with ice and place it on top of the bowl. What happens inside the glass bowl?

   The sides steam up and water condenses on the bottom of

   the pie plate.

   _____

3. **Observe** After several minutes, lift the pie plate. What do you see?

   More water has condensed on the bottom.

   _____

Conclusion

1. **Use Models** What process in nature does this activity model?

   the water cycle/rain

2. **Infer** Why is the pie plate full of ice a necessary part of this activity?

   It stops the rising hot air and cools it, allowing

   water to condense. Without the pie plate, the air would just

   rise out of the bowl.

Name _____ Date _____

Class Cornucopia

Skill: Use Models

Materials

- pencil

Procedure

1. **Collaborate** As a class, compile a list of foods that you might eat in a day. What are some ingredients found in these foods?

   Answers will vary.

   _____

   _____

2. **Collaborate** What are some of the energy sources for these ingredients?

   Sample answers: the Sun, plants, chicken feed

   _____

3. **Use Models** As a class, create a food web showing the ingredients listed and their energy sources.

Conclusion

1. **Use Models** Based on your model, what can you say about how energy moves through the environment?

   Energy moves through the biosphere as plants use energy

   from the Sun and animals eat plants or other animals.

   _____

2. **Infer** What is the original source of energy for all the ingredients?

   the Sun

116

Use with page B23

Comparing Climates

Skill: Use Numbers

Materials

• local temperature and precipitation data

Procedure

1. **Use Numbers** Your teacher will display a climate graph for your region on the board. What relationship between temperature and precipitation do you observe in the climate graph?

   Answers will vary depending on the data shown in

   the graph.

2. **Predict** What would a climate graph for the desert look like?

   Answers will vary; students will probably suggest higher

   temperatures and smaller amounts of precipitation.

3. **Predict** What would a climate graph for an arctic region look like?

   Answers will vary; students will probably predict lower

   temperatures.

Conclusion

1. **Analyze Data** What biome is best described by the graph your teacher made in step 1?

   Answers will vary depending on the location.

2. **Infer** What do you think it means if the climate graphs for two different locations are similar?

   If climate graphs are similar, then the areas are in the same

   biome.

Name _____ Date _____

Comparing Bones

Skill: Measure

Materials

- owl pellets
- metric ruler
- disposable gloves

Procedure

1. **Observe** Watch as your teacher demonstrates how an owl pellet can be broken apart to determine what the owl ate.

2. **Collaborate** Work in small groups. Observe an owl pellet. Measure and observe the bones contained in the pellet. Record your observations below.

Answers will vary.

_____

_____

_____

3. **Communicate** Report your observations to the class. Compare the contents of the owl pellets observed by different groups.

Conclusion

1. **Infer** What did the owl eat? Explain how you inferred this.

Based on the bones, the owl ate one or more small mammals.

_____

_____

2. **Draw Conclusions** What do you know about an owl's role in its ecosystem?

The owl is a predator (carnivore).

_____

_____

Shade of Color

Skill: Use Models

Materials

- construction paper circles of various colors

Procedure

1. **Observe** Watch as your teacher holds up paper circles of various colors. What do you observe when two similar-colored circles are held against one another?

   Students may note that it is difficult to distinguish the

   colors when they are similar.

2. **Observe** What do you observe when two different-colored circles are held against one another?

   Students may note that it is easy to distinguish the two

   circles because they are different colors.

Conclusion

1. **Use Models** What did this activity model? Name an animal that is the same color as its environment.

   This activity modeled how an animal can blend into its

   environment. Sample answers: A white rabbit blends into

   a snowy environment. A green bug is camouflaged when it

   sits on a leaf.

2. **Analyze Data** Why would it be an advantage for an animal to be a color similar to its environment?

   It would make it more difficult for predators to see

   the animal.

Use with page B57

Join the Food Chain

Materials

• pencil

Procedure

1. **Collaborate** Your teacher will ask the entire class to stand and will write the total number of students on the board.

2. **Use Numbers** Calculate the number of students that make up 10 percent of the total. Hint: Multiply the total number of students by 0.10. Answers will vary depending upon the number of students in the class.

3. **Collaborate** Your teacher will ask 10 percent of the students to remain standing while the rest of the class sits down. This activity models the amount of energy transferred from each level of a food chain to the next higher level.

4. **Infer** How efficient is it to be a consumer at each level of the food chain?

   Sample answer: Each level of the food chain has less

   available energy, so it is more efficient to be a lower-level

   consumer than a top-level consumer.

Conclusion

1. **Infer** Where in the food chain is most of the Sun's energy concentrated?

   Most of the Sun's energy is concentrated in

   producers (the lowest level of the food chain).

2. **Infer** What conclusions can you draw about the best sources of human food from the information you learned in this activity?

   Students may infer that humans should mostly eat

   food from the lower levels because it is most plentiful.

Use with page B71

Community Regeneration

Materials

- pencil

Procedure

1. **Collaborate** Your teacher will describe the effects of a volcanic eruption on a community. Each group of students will be assigned a task for rebuilding the community. With your group, make a plan to accomplish your task. Record your plan here.

   Students' plans should provide a clear explanation
   _____

   for how the task is to be accomplished.
   _____

   _____

   _____

2. **Communicate** Present your plan to the class. After hearing each group's plan, work as a class to make a list showing the order in which the tasks should be performed. As a class, the students should develop a logical order for the work.

Conclusion

1. **Infer** On a separate sheet of paper, create a flow chart to display the steps that will restore the community. Branch the chart to divide public and private projects. Charts should present a logical series of steps for recovery that covers the entire community.

2. **Communicate** Below your flow chart, write a brief article for the local newspaper that explains the plan to residents. Articles should include a clear explanation of why each step in the plan is necessary.

Use with page B81

Mineral Hardness

Materials

• 2 unknown mineral samples

Procedure

1. **Collaborate** Work in groups. Each group will examine a pair of unknown minerals.

2. **Observe** Take turns using one of the minerals to scratch the other. Then, use the second mineral to scratch the first. Record your observations below.

   Answers will vary.
   _____

3. **Communicate** Discuss your observations with your group. Then, report your group's results to the class. Your teacher will record all the results on the board.

Conclusion

1. **Compare** Using the results on the board as a guide, list all the mineral samples observed by the class in order from softest to hardest.

   Answers will vary depending upon samples examined.
   _____

   _____

   _____

2. **Predict** Based on your observations, which of the minerals you examined would be able to be scratched by a penny?

   Answers will vary. Students may try this experiment to test it.
   _____

   _____

Use with page C5

Name _____   Date _____

Rock Classes

Skill: Observe

Materials

- Rock Identification Key
- rock sample

Procedure

1. **Observe** Work with a small group. Observe your group's rock sample.

2. **Record Data** Using the Rock Identification Key, identify the rock. What rock does your group have?

   Answers will vary.

3. **Communicate** Present your sample to the class and describe how you arrived at your conclusion.

Safety
• Tell students not to run their fingers along sharp edges. Tell students to be careful not to breathe in dust from the samples or get dust in their eyes.

Conclusion

1. **Compare** Describe how the three classes of rock are different in appearance.

   Sedimentary rock looks like grains stuck together. Igneous rock looks like hardened liquid with a texture that can be smooth or crystalline. Metamorphic rock looks like bent sedimentary rock.

2. **Hypothesize** How could your rock sample have formed?

   Answers will vary. Sample answers: Sedimentary rock forms from sediment compacting together. Metamorphic rock forms when any type of rock is subjected to heat and pressure. Igneous rock forms from cooling magma.

Name _____ Date _____

Your Hand as a Fossil

Skill: Infer

Materials
- paper
- pencil

Procedure

1. **Prepare** As a class, discuss ways that scientists use fossils. What are some things a scientist might be able to learn from a fossil?

   Sample answers: the environment in which the organism lived, the foods the organism ate, the climate of the area in the past

2. **Experiment** Trace your hand on a sheet of paper. After your tracing is complete, hold up your tracing so the class can see.

3. **Observe** Look closely at the tracings made by the students in your class. What observations can you make about the tracings?

   Sample answers: Students have five fingers. Students' hands vary somewhat in size.

Conclusion

Infer What might a scientist in the future infer about humans based on their hand tracings?

Sample answers: Most humans had five fingers. Humans used writing tools. Most, but not all, humans used their right hands to draw.

Use with page C33

Name _____ Date _____

Make Your Own Pangaea

Materials

- construction paper cut in the shape of the continents

Procedure

1. **Hypothesize** Look at the model of the continents your teacher has prepared. Based on their shapes, describe how they might have once fit together as a supercontinent called Pangaea.

   Students should note that the coastlines of South America

   and Africa fit together like puzzle pieces.

2. **Use Models** Your teacher will move the pieces of the model to show how the continents might have fit together.

3. **Predict** The continental plates are still moving. How do you think the continents will look 1,000 years from today?

   Answers will vary, but should reflect that the continents will

   be in a different position 1,000 years from now.

Conclusion

1. **Use Models** As a class, form a theory about the position of the continents 1,000 years from today. How might the conditions on the continents be different if they were in these new positions?

   Answers will vary, but should reflect an understanding of

   the effect of a continent's position on its climate.

2. **Infer** Based on its location in Pangaea, explain how the climate of North America might have changed from 200 million years ago.

   Sample answer: Most of what is now North America was

   located in equatorial regions when it was part of Pangaea.

   Therefore, the climate probably was once much warmer.

Use with page C43

Books as Plates

Skill: Use Models

Materials

- two textbooks
- two spiral-bound notebooks

Procedure

1. **Use Models** Your teacher will slide the edges of two textbooks past one another to model plate movement.

2. **Predict** Your teacher will show you two spiral-bound notebooks. What do you think will happen when your teacher slides the edges of the notebooks past one another?

   The spirals will get caught in one another, making it difficult

   to slide the notebooks.

3. **Observe** Watch as your teacher slides the spiral-bound notebooks past one another. Was your prediction correct?

   Sample answer: yes

Conclusion

1. **Analyze Data** Which model better represents the movement of Earth's plates? Why?

   The spiral notebook model more accurately represents

   Earth's plates, because the edges of Earth's plates are not

   smooth.

2. **Communicate** Explain how you think earthquakes are caused when pressure builds up at edges of moving plates.

   Answers will vary, but should demonstrate a general

   understanding of the concept of what happens at plate

   boundaries.

Use with page C51

Name _____ Date _____

Comparing Consumption

Skill: Use Numbers

Materials

• 4 containers of the same size

Procedure

1. **Use Numbers** Split into two groups, one consisting of five percent of the class and the other consisting of the remaining students.

2. **Collaborate** The smaller group will hold one container. This group represents the population of the United States. The larger group will hold three containers. This group represents the rest of the world's population.

3. **Use Models** The containers represent the amount of oil each group consumes. Compare the oil consumption per person in the two groups.

   In the smaller group, consumption per person is about

   three times higher.

Conclusion

1. **Use Numbers** In 2003, the world used 80 million barrels of oil per day. The United States uses one-quarter of the world's oil. About how much oil does the United States use each day?

   80 million × 0.25 = 20 million. The United States uses about

   20 million barrels of oil each day.

2. **Hypothesize** How can people extend Earth's supply of oil?

   People can conserve their use of oil and find new sources

   of energy.

Use with page C67

Name _____ Date _____

More Light, More Power

Skill: Use Models

Materials

- solar panel with wires and clips
- sunlight or powerful light bulb
- motor with fan

Procedure

1. **Prepare** Your teacher will set up a solar panel connected to a motor with a fan.

2. **Observe** Describe what happens to the fan when the solar panel is exposed to light.

   The fan moves.

   _____

3. **Record Data** What happens to the fan when your teacher covers up part of the panel? Why does this happppen?

   The fan slows down. Less energy is being converted by the

   solar panel.

Conclusion

1. **Infer** Use your knowledge of electricity to explain your observations of the solar panel, the wires, and the fan.

   The solar panel uses light to produce electricity. The current

   travels in a loop through the wires and powers the fan.

2. **Hypothesize** What do you think would happen if your teacher connected more solar panels to the motor?

   The motor would spin faster with more power from more

   panels.

Name _____ Date _____

Uneven Heating

Skill: Record Data

Materials

- two containers
- soil
- water
- thermometer

Procedure

1. **Record Data** Your teacher will measure the temperature of a container of water and a container of soil every 30 minutes for an hour. Record the data in the chart below.

Time (minutes)	Soil Temp. (°C)	Water Temp. (°C)
0		
30		
60		

2. **Observe** How does the temperature of the soil change? How does the temperature of the water change?

Students should see that the temperature of the soil

increases more.

Conclusion

1. **Predict** What would happen if the containers were left in the sun all day?

Answers will vary. Students should predict that the soil

would heat up more and that the water would continue to

heat up at a slower rate.

2. **Infer** Based on the results of your experiment, which do you think heats up faster, land or the ocean?

land

Use with page D5

Effect of Spinning

Skill: Infer

Materials

- globe
- chalk

Procedure

1. **Observe** Your teacher will try to draw a straight line on the globe while the globe is spinning. What happens to the line?

   The line bends as the globe is spun.

   _____

2. **Use Models** What does the spinning globe represent?

   Earth spinning on its axis; Earth's rotation

   _____

Conclusion

1. **Infer** How do you think the spinning globe and the curved line relate to the way that Earth's rotation affects winds and ocean currents?

   Winds and currents do not move in straight lines, because

   of Earth's rotation.

   _____

2. **Infer** Based on the results of your experiment, what would happen if a line were drawn from the South Pole to the equator?

   The line would bend in the opposite direction.

   _____

Name _____ Date _____

Predicting the Weather

Skill: Predict

Materials

• weather reports from last 5 days

Procedure

1. **Collaborate** Work in small groups. Your teacher will provide weather reports for the last 5 days. Observe and discuss the weather data.

2. **Analyze Data** Do you see any patterns in the weather data? Record your observations below.

   Answers will vary. _____

   _____

3. **Predict** Based on your analysis of the data, predict what the weather will be like tomorrow. Record your prediction below.

   Predictions will vary. _____

   _____

   _____

Conclusion

1. **Compare** How accurate was your prediction about what the weather would be like?

   Answers will vary. Have students compare each variable

   when answering the question. _____

   _____

2. **Infer** Based on your data, can you predict what the weather will be like next week? Why or why not?

   The weather is difficult to predict accurately beyond two or

   three days. _____

Name _____ Date _____

Shadows and Sundials

Materials

- sundial
- watch or clock

Safety
• Caution
students
not to look
directly at
the Sun.
It can
damage
their eyes.

Procedure

1. **Hypothesize** Form a hypothesis to explain how the changing length of shadows relates to the Sun's position.

   Answers will vary. Students should hypothesize that shadows

   change due to the angle of the Sun's rays, with shadows

   becoming shorter as the Sun gets higher in the sky.

2. **Observe** Your teacher will demonstrate how a sundial can be used to show time. Every hour, record the time and your observations of the gnomon's shadow.

   Observations will vary; students should note the change in

   the gnomon's shadow over time.

Conclusion

1. **Analyze Data** Do the collected data support the hypothesis you made in step 1? Why or why not?

   Answers will vary. Students will probably say that the

   collected data support their hypotheses; the gnomon's

   shadow was shorter when the Sun was high in the sky.

2. **Infer** Do you think the shadows on the sundial would fall in exactly the same positions every day of the year?

   No, the lengths of the shadows on the sundial are affected

   by the relative position of the Sun in the sky during

   different seasons.

Use with page D45

Board Eclipses

Skill: Infer

Materials

- basketball
- flashlight
- chalk

Procedure

1. **Observe** Your teacher will draw a small circle on the board and use a flashlight to demonstrate how a basketball's shadow can cover the circle. How does this model a lunar eclipse?

   During a lunar eclipse, the Earth blocks the Sun's light from

   the Moon.

2. **Observe** Your teacher will repeat the demonstration, but will increase the size of the circle drawn on the board. How does this model a solar eclipse?

   During a solar eclipse, the Moon blocks the Sun's light from

   Earth.

Conclusion

1. **Analyze Data** When the Moon is between the Sun and Earth, what determines if a solar eclipse occurs?

   the position of the Moon in its orbit

2. **Infer** How can total and partial solar eclipses occur at the same time?

   Depending on where two people are on Earth, they may

   simultaneously see a partial eclipse and a total eclipse.

133

Use with page D55

Name _____ Date _____

Tidal Models

Materials
- orange
- grape
- rubber band

Procedure

1. **Observe** Watch your teacher use the orange, the grape, and the rubber band to model how the Moon causes tides on Earth.

2. **Use Models** Describe a different set of items that could be used to model how the Moon affects Earth's tides. Remember to consider the scale of the items in the model.

Answers will vary. The item selected to represent Earth

should be roughly four times the size of the item selected

to represent the Moon.

Conclusion

1. **Infer** Tides cause the water level on Earth's beaches to change throughout the day. List one way that the changing water level affects a beach.

Sample answers: When the beach is dry, it gets hot; when

the beach is wet, it cools down; the sand shifts and smoothes

out as the water flows over it.

2. **Infer** Think about your answer to question 1. Describe a characteristic that would help organisms live in this changing environment.

Sample answer: the ability to dig into the sand or protect

themselves from drying out when the beach is dry; being

able to withstand the force of the waves

Mini Solar System

Skill: Use Models

Materials

- paper
- tape measure
- scissors

Procedure

1. **Collaborate** Work in a small group. Your teacher will assign each group a planet. Convert the diameter of your planet to the assigned units.

2. **Use Numbers** Now calculate the distance from the Sun to your assigned planet in the chosen units.

3. **Use Models** Using paper, construct a scale model of your planet. **Safety:** Be careful when using scissors.

4. **Collaborate** Use a tape measure to plot the location of your group's assigned planet in the solar system model.

Conclusion

1. **Observe** Look at the positions and sizes of the planets and the Sun. What patterns, if any, do you observe?

   Sample answer: The smaller planets are closer to the Sun.

   There is a large gap between Mars and Jupiter. The larger

   planets are farther from the Sun.

2. **Infer** Based on your answer to question 1, do you think Pluto is a true planet?

   Sample answer: Because of its small size and great

   distance from the Sun, Pluto may not be a true planet.

Use with page D75

Name _____ Date _____

Dim or Bright?

Skill: Compare

Materials

- flashlights

Procedure

1. **Observe** Your teacher will shine two flashlights from the back of the room to the front of the room. Compare the brightnesses of the light cast by the two flashlights. Record your observations here.

   Students should observe two lights of brightness.

   _____

2. **Observe** Your teacher will again shine two flashlights from the back of the room to the front of the room. Compare the brightnesses of the light cast by the two flashlights.

   Students should observe one bright light and one dim light.

   _____

3. **Compare** Your teacher will shine the two flashlights from step 1 again, but this time the flashlights will be in different locations. How does this compare to what you observed in step 1?

   Students should observe that this time the lights do not

   appear to have the same brightness.

Conclusion

1. **Communicate** What factors affect the brightness of a star?

   distance and how bright the star actually is

2. **Hypothesize** What can you tell about two stars that appear equally bright from Earth?

   Either they are equally distant with equal absolute magnitude

   or one star has greater absolute magnitude but is farther

   from Earth.

Use with page D87

Model an Atom

Materials

- pebble

Procedure

1. **Collaborate** Work in small groups. Stand in a circle. Have one group member place a pebble in the middle of the circle.

2. **Use Models** You have made a model of an atom. In your model, what part of the atom does the pebble represent?

the nucleus
_____

Conclusion

1. **Analyze Data** The diameter of an actual nucleus is about one ten-thousandth ($\frac{1}{10,000}$) of the diameter of the actual atom. To make your model more accurate, should the item representing the nucleus be smaller or larger than the pebble your group used to represent the nucleus?

smaller
_____

_____

2. **Infer** Think about your model. What makes up most of the volume of an atom?

empty space
_____

_____

Use with page E5

Make Tarnish Vanish

Skill: Compare

Materials

- three pennies
- strong vinegar solution

Procedure

1. **Observe** Examine the three pennies provided by your teacher. What do you observe about the pennies?

   Two are dull and tarnished, one is bright and shiny.

2. **Predict** Your teacher will place one of the tarnished pennies in a strong vinegar solution. What do you predict will happen?

   Possible answer: The penny will look cleaner and shinier.

3. **Observe** Examine the pennies again. Record your observations.

   The penny placed in vinegar is brighter than the other dull

   penny, but maybe not as bright as the new one.

Conclusion

1. **Compare** Compare the properties of the penny before and after it was placed in the vinegar solution.

   Properties noted should be physical, such as color, texture,

   and size. The tarnish disappeared or was diminished after

   the penny was placed in the vinegar.

2. **Infer** Older pennies have a coating of copper oxide (CuO) that makes them look darker and duller than a new penny. What can you infer about the effect of the vinegar solution on this coating?

   The solution causes the coating to dissolve.

Sugar Stir

Materials

- 2 beakers, each containing 200 ml of water
- 30 ml of granulated sugar, divided into 15 ml portions
- 1 stirring rod or spoon
- stopwatch

Procedure

1. **Collaborate** Work with the members of your assigned group.

2. **Experiment** Your teacher will give each group a beaker containing water. Add 15 ml of granulated sugar to the water. Students in group A should stir the mixture for 60 seconds.

3. **Observe** Compare the remaining sugar crystals in the stirred and unstirred beakers. Record your observations.

   Students should observe that in the stirred beaker, more or

   all of the sugar will have dissolved.

Conclusion

1. **Analyze Data** Did stirring increase or decrease the rate at which the sugar dissolved?

   Stirring increased the rate at which the sugar dissolved.

2. **Hypothesize** How do you think stirring affects the rate at which sugar dissolves?

   Stirring increases the rate of contact between water

   molecules and sugar particles, which increases the rate of

   dissolving.

Do a Litmus Test

Skill: Classify

Materials

- red and blue litmus paper
- vinegar solution
- baking soda solution

Procedure

1. **Observe** Your teacher will test red litmus paper and blue litmus paper in a vinegar solution. Record your observations here.

   The blue litmus paper turns red in the vinegar solution.

   _____

2. **Observe** Your teacher will test red litmus paper and blue litmus paper in a baking soda solution. Record your observations here.

   The red litmus paper turns blue in the baking soda solution.

   _____

Conclusion

1. **Classify** Blue litmus paper turns red in the presence of an acid. Red litmus paper turns blue in the presence of a base. Classify each solution as an acid or a base.

   Vinegar solution is an acid. Baking soda solution is a base.

   _____

2. **Infer** Based on your observations, do you think foods that are acids taste sour or bitter? Base your answer on your observations; do not taste either solution.

   Foods that taste acids are sour.

   _____

Balloons on a Bottle

Skill: Hypothesize

Materials

- medium-sized balloon
- plastic bottle
- hot and cold water

Safety
• Make sure that the hot water is not too hot to touch.

Procedure

1. **Prepare** Stretch the opening of the balloon over the opening of a plastic bottle so that the bottle is sealed.

2. **Observe** Hold the bottle under hot water. What happened?

   The balloon expanded.

3. **Observe** Hold the bottle under cold water. What happened to the balloon?

   The balloon contracted.

Conclusion

1. **Hypothesize** Why did the balloon behave the way it did in hot and cold water?

   Air expands when it is heated and contracts when it is

   cooled.

2. **Predict** Based on your observations, what would happen if the balloon were placed in warm water?

   The balloon would inflate a little because the air

   would expand some.

Mixing It Up

Skill: Observe

Materials

- 3 plastic cups
- sugar
- sand
- antacid tablet
- water

Safety
- Do not allow the students to eat or taste the antacid tablet.

Procedure

1. **Prepare** Fill three plastic cups one-quarter full with water.

2. **Observe** Drop a spoonful of sand into one cup, a spoonful of sugar into another, and an antacid tablet into the third.

3. **Record Data** Record your observations.

The sand sank. The sugar dissolved. The antacid bubbled.

_____

_____

Conclusion

1. **Analyze Data** Which of the observations showed a physical change? Which showed a chemical change?

The sand and the sugar showed physical changes. The

antacid showed a chemical change.

_____

2. **Predict** What do you think would happen if the water in the cups were warmer?

The sand would react the same way, the sugar would

dissolve faster, and the antacid would begin to undergo a

chemical change faster. All the reactions would be sped up.

Name _____ Date _____

Escaping Gas Mass

Skill: Compare

Materials

- 1-liter plastic soda bottle
- 3 effervescent tablets
- balance

Safety
• Remind
students not
to eat the
effervescent
tablets.

Procedure

1. **Prepare** Fill a 1-liter plastic soda bottle one-quarter full of water. Measure the total mass of the bottle, its lid, the water, and the three effervescent tablets.

   Masses will vary.

2. **Observe** Break the three effervescent tablets into pieces and place them in the bottle. Quickly seal the bottle and place it on the balance. What happens to the mass?

   The mass remains the same.

3. **Observe** Unseal the bottle and place it on the balance. How did the mass change?

   The mass decreased.

Conclusion

1. **Hypothesize** Why did the mass change after the bottle was opened?

   The escaping gas led to a decrease in the overall mass.

2. **Infer** Based on your observations, why does soda go flat after it has been left open for a while?

   The effervescent bubbles escape, leaving only the

   soda behind.

Get the Ball Rolling

Skill: Compare

Materials

- cardboard
- stack of books
- ball

Procedure

1. **Observe** Your teacher will construct a ramp by leaning a piece of cardboard against a stack of books and will release a ball at the top of the ramp. Watch how fast the ball rolls down the ramp.

2. **Compare** Your teacher will change the angle of the ramp by removing books from the stack. How does the speed of the ball change?

   It slows down as books are removed.

Conclusion

1. **Infer** What is the relationship between the steepness of the ramp and the rolling speed?

   The steeper the ramp, the faster the ball rolls.

2. **Predict** Based on your observations, what would happen if your teacher added more books to the stack?

   The ramp would be steeper and the ball would roll down

   faster than during any of the other trials.

Name _____ Date _____

Water Waves

Skill: Record Data

Materials

- small stone
- balance
- large stone
- pan of water

Procedure

1. **Record Data** Your teacher will measure the mass of a small stone. Record the mass below.

Masses will vary.

2. **Predict** What do you think will happen when your teacher drops the stone in the pan of water?

Answers will vary. Students will probably recognize that the

stone will make circular waves in the water.

3. **Observe** Record what happens when your teacher drops the stone.

The stone made waves in the water.

4. **Record Data** Your teacher will repeat the experiment with a larger stone. Record the mass of the stone and what happens when it hits the water.

The waves were bigger with the larger stone.

Conclusion

1. **Infer** What is the relationship between the size of the stone and the waves it creates?

The larger the stone, the larger the waves.

2. **Predict** What do you think would happen if the stone were dropped from a height of 2 meters above the water? From a height of 3 centimeters above the water?

The greater the height, the bigger the waves.

Name _____ Date _____

Boiling Bubbles

Materials

- liquid soap with glycol stearate
- plastic container
- food coloring
- water
- hot water or warm surface

Procedure

1. **Prepare** Your teacher will mix one part soap with four parts water in the plastic container and will add a few drops of food coloring to the container.

2. **Experiment** Watch as your teacher places the container over the hot water or other heat source.

3. **Communicate** Describe what you see when you look at the plastic container from above.

   Students will see convection occurring as the material

   moves up and down, like a slow boil.

Conclusion

1. **Hypothesize** Why do the bubbles form?

   The water in the bottom of the container heats up and rises.

   This creates a convection current.

2. **Predict** Based on your observations, what do you think would happen if more heat were added?

   The bubbles would form more quickly.

146

Use with page F23

Name _____ Date _____

Spin the Wheel

Skill: Predict

Materials

• posterboard color wheel

Procedure

1. **Predict** Observe the color wheel that your teacher has made. Your teacher will spin the wheel slowly. What do you think you will see? Record your prediction.

   Students may predict that each color can still be seen.

   _____

2. **Observe** Watch the color wheel as your teacher spins it slowly.

3. **Predict** What do you think you will see if your teacher spins the wheel quickly? Record your prediction.

   Students may predict that the colors will blend into white.

   _____

4. **Experiment** Watch the color wheel as your teacher spins it quickly.

Conclusion

1. **Communicate** Describe your observations of the color wheel when it was spinning slowly and when it was spinning rapidly.

   Sample answer: As the wheel was spinning slowly, each

   color could be seen. As the wheel began to spin faster, the

   colors blended into white.

2. **Infer** What might explain the appearance of the color wheel when it was spinning rapidly?

   White light is made of all the colors.

Laser Beam Interactions

Skill: Infer

Materials

- laser beam
- glass
- prism
- mirror

Procedure

1. **Observe** Your teacher will shine a laser at various objects.

2. **Record Data** What do you observe when your teacher shines a laser beam through a piece of clear glass?

   The laser beam is transmitted by the glass.

   _____

3. **Record Data** What do you observe when your teacher shines a laser beam through a prism?

   The laser beam is refracted.

   _____

4. **Record Data** What do you observe when your teacher shines a laser beam toward a mirror?

   The laser beam is reflected.

   _____

Conclusion

1. **Analyze Data** Describe the ways that the laser beam behaved when it interacted with each object.

   Sample answers: Most of the laser light was transmitted by

   the glass, refracted by the prism, and reflected by the mirror.

2. **Infer** Why does the laser beam act as it did?

   Different materials cause light to behave in different ways.

Name _____ Date _____

Modify a Circuit

Skill: Use Variables

Materials

- battery
- wires
- 2 light bulbs

Procedure

1. **Observe** Your teacher will set up a circuit with one bulb. When your teacher closes the circuit, observe the brightness of the bulb. Record your observations below.

   Students should observe that the one bulb is brightly lit.

2. **Predict** What effect do you think adding a bulb would have on the brightness of the bulbs?

   Students may predict that the bulbs would dim.

3. **Use Variables** What variable would you change in order to test your prediction in step 2?

   the number of bulbs in the circuit

4. **Record Data** Your teacher will add a bulb to the circuit. Record your observations below. Was your prediction correct?

   The bulbs are dimmer.

   _____

Conclusion

1. **Analyze Data** What determined the brightness of the bulb in each step?

   The number of bulbs in the circuit.

2. **Infer** The number of bulbs was the independent variable in this experiment. What was the dependent variable?

   the brightness of the bulbs

Name _____ Date _____

Strength of Magnetic Forces

Skill: Hypothesize

Materials

- compass
- circuit
- ruler or tape measure

Procedure

1. **Collaborate** Work with a group. Your teacher will assign each group a distance. Have one group member hold the compass at your assigned distance from the wire in the circuit that your teacher has set up. Record your observations below.

   Observations will vary depending on distance.

2. **Communicate** Report your group's observations to the class. Your teacher will record the data on the board.

3. **Hypothesize** Form a hypothesis about how the distance from the wire affects the strength of the magnetic force acting on the compass. Record your hypothesis below.

   Students should note that the strength of the force

   decreases as distance increases.

Conclusion

Compare How does the effect of the current in the wire compare to the effect of Earth's magnetic field on the compass?

The current in the wire had a greater effect on the

compass than Earth's magnetic field.

150

Use with page F81

Name _____ Date _____

Open Parachute!

Skill: Predict

Materials

- 2 metal washers
- string
- plastic bag
- tape

Procedure

1. **Predict** Your teacher has tied a metal washer to a parachute made from a plastic bag. If a plain washer and the washer with the parachute are dropped from shoulder height at the same time, which do you think will hit the floor first?

2. **Observe** Watch as your teacher drops the washers. Record your observations below. Was your prediction correct?

   The washer with the parachute falls more slowly.

3. **Experiment** Your teacher will repeat the experiment, varying the height from which the washers are dropped. Predict what will happen. Record your predictions and observations below.

   The greater the height from which the parachute and plain washers are

   dropped, the greater the difference in time when they hit the ground.

Conclusion

1. **Hypothesize** Form a hypothesis to explain how a parachute works. Propose an experiment to test this hypothesis.

   A parachute increases resistance to motion through air. To

   test the hypothesis, students could punch small holes in

   the plastic bag. The parachute will fall more quickly.

2. **Predict** When are parachutes most useful? Describe a situation where a parachute would not be useful to slow someone's rate of falling.

   Parachutes are used to slow falling objects so they hit the

   ground gently. They are not useful very close to the ground.

Sliding Books

Materials

- paperback book
- heavy textbook

Procedure

1. **Observe** Your teacher will push a paperback book along a table. Why did the book move? Why did it stop?

   A force made it move, and another force made it stop.

   _____

2. **Predict** Your teacher will place a heavy textbook on the table. What will happen if the textbook is pushed with the same amount of force as the paperback book?

   Answers will vary, but students should recognize that the

   textbook will not move as far.

3. **Experiment** Watch as your teacher pushes the textbook. How far did the textbook move?

   not as far as the paperback book moved

Conclusion

1. **Infer** Why did the paperback move farther than the textbook?

   It does not have as much mass.

2. **Infer** Based on the results of your experiment, what is the relationship between force, mass, and motion?

   The same amount of force will move a small object farther

   than an object with greater mass.

Pulley That Weight!

Skill: Hypothesize

Materials

- simple pulley
- 500-gram mass
- four-pulley system

Procedure

1. **Observe** Your teacher will ask a student to lift a 500-gram mass. Then, the teacher will ask the student to lift the mass using a simple pulley, and then using a four-pulley system. The student will describe any difference in the effort required to lift the mass.

2. **Record Data** On the line below, record which method was the easiest way to lift the weight.

   It was easiest to lift the mass with the four-pulley system.

   _____

Conclusion

1. **Infer** Based on the results of your experiment, what is one thing pulleys can be used for?

   to lift heavy objects

   _____

2. **Hypothesize** How do pulleys change the force needed to lift objects? Form a hypothesis about the way a pulley works.

   A pulley makes it easier to lift a load. In a pulley system,

   the load is divided among the strands of rope; less force is

   needed to lift objects.

How Do Scientists Classify Organisms?

1. **Main Idea** What are two goals of the system used to classify organisms?

   to give an organism a name recognized by scientists

   worldwide, to group organisms by characteristics

2. **Vocabulary** What is biological classification?

   It is a system that organizes living things into groups.

3. **Reading Skill: Classify** You are trying to identify a one-celled organism. You know that the organism has a cell nucleus and produces its own food from sunlight. What kingdom does the organism belong to?

   It belongs to the protist kingdom.

4. **Critical Thinking: Evaluate** Scientists once classified living things into only two kingdoms: Plants and Animals. Why do you think they use six kingdoms today?

   Sample answer: Some organisms lacked characteristics

   associated with either kingdom.

5. **Inquiry Skill: Compare** What are two differences between organisms in Kingdom Protista and Kingdom Fungi?

   Most protists can move, and fungi cannot. Fungi get

   nutrients by decomposing organic matter, and protists

   create their own food.

Test Prep

The smallest and most specialized level of classification is

A kingdom.

B phylum.

C species.

D class.

How Are Plants Classified?

1. Main Idea What are two main characteristics scientists use when classifying plants?

Scientists use how the plants transport water and how they

reproduce when classifying plants.

2. Vocabulary Define *vascular* as it relates to plants.

Vascular plants have tube-like tissues that transport water

and nutrients.

3. Reading Skill: Compare and Contrast How are angiosperms and gymnosperms different?

Angiosperms produce flowers, fruit, and seeds.

Gymnosperms produce seeds, but no flowers or fruits.

4. Critical Thinking: Evaluate Is the following statement accurate? "Plants produce fruits to provide food for animals."

No, plants produce fruits to protect and nourish seeds.

5. Inquiry Skill: Classify Would it be possible to identify a plant as either vascular or nonvascular by looking at tissues from the plant under a microscope?

Yes, vascular plants would have visible vascular tissues.

Test Prep

Angiosperms are

A nonflowering plants.

B one-celled plants.

C nonvascular plants.

D flowering plants.

How Are Animals Classified?

1. **Main Idea** Describe the diversity of the animal kingdom.

   Animals come in different shapes, skin coverings, body

   structures, and body temperatures.

2. **Vocabulary** Define *invertebrate* and *vertebrate*. Compare the two groups of animals.

   Invertebrates are animals that lack a backbone. Vertebrates

   are animals that have a backbone.

3. **Reading Skill: Main Idea and Details** Describe six different kinds of invertebrates.

   sponges: radial symmetry, shapeless bodies; cnidarians: radial

   symmetry, true mouth; echinoderms: radial symmetry, use

   feet suckers to capture prey; worms: bilateral symmetry,

   clearly defined head; mollusks: bilateral symmetry, soft

   bodies, sometimes a shell; arthropods: bilateral symmetry,

   shells, jointed appendages

4. **Critical Thinking: Synthesis** What could you conclude if you observed an animal with feathers that couldn't fly? Is the animal a bird? Explain.

   Birds are the only animals with feathers, so the animal

   would have to be a bird. Not all birds can fly.

5. **Inquiry Skill: Communicate** (See page A37.) Charts should show levels of vertebrate classification.

Test Prep

Soft-bodied animals that may have a hard shell are called

A sponges.   **B** echinoderms.   **C** mollusks.   **D** mammals.

Use with page A37

What Do Cells Do?

1. **Main Idea** What do cells need to stay alive?

   Cells need food, water, and a way to eliminate wastes.

   _____

2. **Vocabulary** Use the terms *chloroplast* and *organelle* in a sentence that describes cell function.

   Sample answer: A chloroplast is an organelle in plant cells

   that manufactures food for the plant.

3. **Reading Skill: Draw Conclusions** Could a cell survive without its mitochondria if all the other organelles were present?

   No, because the mitochondria provide energy to the cell.

4. **Critical Thinking: Analyze** What are the parts of a cell? How do cell parts work together to keep the cell alive?

   cell membrane, cytoplasm, organelles; membrane: lets

   material in and out and keeps cell in one piece; cytoplasm:

   stores, transports; organelles: feed cell and perform other

   essential tasks

5. **Inquiry Skill: Use Models** Describe a model you could use to demonstrate the process of diffusion.

   Sample answer: A model could be a drop of food coloring

   in water.

Test Prep

To make food, plants use a process called

A photosynthesis.

B cell division.

C mitosis.

D mitochondria.

157

Use with page A51

How Are Cells Specialized?

1. Main Idea What are specialized cells?

Cells that have the ability to perform certain tasks are
specialized cells.

2. Vocabulary Define *tissue*. Use this word in a sentence that describes how organisms accomplish tasks.

Sample answer: Tissue is a group of cells with the same
structure and function. Epithelial tissue protects surfaces.

3. Reading Skill: Main Idea and Details Describe the interaction between two human organ systems that work together.

Sample answer: The respiratory system brings oxygen into
the body; the circulatory system carries it to cells.

4. Critical Thinking: Evaluate Would it be accurate to say that all multicellular organisms have the same type and number of organs? Explain.

No, different species might have different needs, so the
organs will be different.

5. Inquiry Skill: Use Models How is the nervous system like a set of telephone wires?

The nervous system sends information and signals to and
from the brain.

Test Prep

The brain is part of the

A musculoskeletal system.

B urinary system.

C circulatory system.

D nervous system.

Name _____ Date _____

How Does Disease Affect Cells?

1. **Main Idea** What causes infectious and non-infectious diseases?

   infectious diseases: bacteria and viruses; non-infectious

   diseases: body systems not working properly

2. **Vocabulary** What is the immune system? Give an example of how the immune system works.

   The immune system has cells that travel through the body

   and fight harmful foreign organisms. When a harmful

   organism invades the body, the immune system produces

   cells to attack and destroy it.

3. **Reading Skill: Cause and Effect** How does the immune system fight viruses that invade the body?

   It produces antibodies to fight viral infection.

4. **Critical Thinking: Draw Conclusions** You notice that you get more colds when you don't wash your hands very often. What conclusion can you draw from this?

   Washing hands cleans off the viruses and bacteria.

5. **Inquiry Skill: Infer** Doctors sometimes use computer models to track the spread of an infectious disease. How might this help them better understand how to prevent the disease?

   They can find connections among the people who

   contract the disease to determine who is at risk.

Test Prep

Special proteins produced by the body to fight viruses are called

A antibodies.

B spirochetes.

C bacteria.

D medicine.

How Do Organisms Reproduce and Grow?

1. **Main Idea** Why doesn't cell division result in two cells with half the needed number of chromosomes?

   During interphase, the cell copies each chromosome.

2. **Vocabulary** How are sexual reproduction and asexual reproduction different?

   In asexual reproduction, one parent produces identical

   offspring. In sexual reproduction, two parents produce

   offspring that inherit traits from each.

3. **Reading Skill: Sequence** During which phase of mitosis do the chromosomes pull apart and begin to form two new cells?

   during anaphase

4. **Critical Thinking: Apply** How do people use selective breeding to change a species?

   by breeding only individuals that have the desired traits

5. **Inquiry Skill: Observe** Look at the photo of the sheep on A84. What traits other than color might a sheep rancher choose to breed for?

   A rancher may choose to breed sheep whose wool is easier to

   spin into yarn.

Test Prep

Asexual reproduction results in offspring with traits that are

A similar to those of one parent.

B identical to those of one parent.

C unique to only the offspring.

D a combination of the traits of two parents.

Use with page A85

How Do Organisms Inherit Traits?

1. **Main Idea** How do genes control an organism's traits?

   DNA sends messages to the cell to direct its activities.

2. **Vocabulary** Write a sentence that uses the terms *genes*, *traits*, and *recessive*.

   Sample answer: A recessive allele for a gene shows up as a

   trait only if both alleles present are recessive.

3. **Reading Skill: Draw Conclusions** Pure white fur color in cats is determined by a single gene that is either dominant or recessive. A cat with orange fur was crossed with a cat with white fur. Two of their kittens have orange fur and two have white fur. What does this show about the parent cats?

   One parent was a hybrid (e.g., Cc) and the other had two

   recessive alleles (cc).

4. **Critical Thinking: Apply** Suppose two white sheep have several sets of offspring. In one set, one of the lambs is black. How would you explain this?

   Despite a 3:1 probability of a black lamb in each flock, each

   outcome (birth) is independent of the others.

5. **Inquiry Skill: Use Models** To model meiosis, why would you use two chenille stems to represent a chromosome, instead of one chenille stem?

   A chromosome is made of two chromatids, and each

   chenille stem would represent one chromatid.

Test Prep

The forms of a gene are called

A alleles.

B chromatids.

C traits.

D chromosomes.

How Is Genetic Information Transferred?

1. Main Idea What two properties of DNA allow it to be copied?

double helix and base pairs

2. Vocabulary How are the roles of DNA and RNA similar? How are they different?

Both contain information. RNA makes it possible to use the

instructions stored in DNA.

3. Reading Skill: Cause and Effect Down syndrome is a genetic disorder. A person with Down syndrome has an extra copy of chromosome 21. What might cause a fertilized cell to gain an extra chromosome?

incorrect separation of chromosomes in meiosis

4. Critical Thinking: Apply How might knowing the human genome allow doctors to determine if someone is likely to develop certain diseases?

Doctors could study an individual's DNA to determine

whether the person carries the gene for the disorder.

5. Inquiry Skill: Classify How can mutations be classified? What characterizes each type of mutation?

gene mutation or chromosomal mutation; gene: one or a few

genes change; chromosomal: entire chromosome changes

Test Prep

During protein synthesis, tRNA

A carries protein building blocks to the protein.

B lets go of the completed protein chain.

C copies information from DNA.

D reads the three-letter code of bases.

What Do Fossils Reveal?

1. **Main Idea** Why are fossils important tools to scientists?

   They show which organisms lived in the past and what the

   environment was like then.

2. **Vocabulary** When do species become extinct?

   when there are no members of the species left alive

3. **Reading Skill: Draw Conclusions** A fossil insect preserved in amber has evidence of pollen grains on its body. What might you conclude about the insect?

   It visited the flower from which the pollen came.

4. **Critical Thinking: Evaluate** What kinds of information may fossilized footprints reveal about an animal? What characteristics or behaviors would not be revealed by fossilized footprints?

   Footprints would give clues to an animal's weight and size, but

   not to how the animal looked.

5. **Inquiry Skill: Compare** What are the differences in the ways scientists analyze trace fossils and fossilized remains of organisms?

   They use trace fossils to determine the organism's behavior

   and fossilized remains to determine body structure.

Test Prep

Studying the fossil of an organism can reveal

A how big the organism was.

B what the organism smelled like.

C how large the population of that type of organism was.

D what time of day the organism usually ate.

How Do Species Change?

1. Main Idea What was Charles Darwin's main contribution to science?

Darwin's main contribution was his theory of evolution, or natural selection.

2. Vocabulary Distinguish between selective breeding and natural selection.

In selective breeding, people choose the traits they want to favor. In natural selection, environmental forces determine which traits survive.

3. Reading Skill: Problem and Solution Darwin noticed that finches on different islands had different beak shapes. What did he determine to be the reason for these differences?

Differences were due to the different food supplies.

4. Critical Thinking: Synthesis What would you conclude if you learned that an elephant and a hyrax, a small rodent-like animal, had similar DNA?

The two organisms shared common ancestors.

5. Inquiry Skill: Infer How might farmers thousands of years ago have developed wheat plants with desirable traits?

They might have kept seeds from plants with desired traits and used those seeds to sow the next crop.

Test Prep

Sources of evidence that organisms evolve over time do NOT include

A DNA evidence.

C the fossil record.

B learned behavior.

D similarities in anatomy.

How Do Oxygen and Carbon Dioxide Cycle?

1. **Main Idea** How do living things depend on the carbon dioxide cycle and the oxygen cycle?

   Both plants and animals need oxygen for respiration, and

   plants need carbon dioxide for photosynthesis.

2. **Vocabulary** Write a sentence that relates the terms *photosynthesis* and *respiration*.

   Sample answer: Photosynthesis is opposite to respiration.

3. **Reading Skill: Compare and Contrast** Why are photosynthesis and respiration opposite processes?

   Photosynthesis uses carbon dioxide and releases oxygen;

   respiration uses oxygen and releases carbon dioxide.

4. **Critical Thinking: Evaluate** Will the amount of carbon dioxide in the atmosphere soon be greater than the amount of oxygen? Explain.

   No, there is much less carbon dioxide than oxygen.

5. **Inquiry Skill: Predict** You blow through a straw into a beaker of water that has algae growing in it. If you then cover the container, what will happen to the level of carbon dioxide over time? Explain your answer.

   It will decrease. The algae will use the carbon dioxide for

   photosynthesis.

Test Prep

Which process provides the oxygen you breathe?

A greenhouse effect   **C** respiration

B deforestation   **D** photosynthesis

How Do Nitrogen and Water Cycle?

1. **Main Idea** Why is the cycling of nitrogen and water so important for life?

   Both substances are necessary for life, so they need to be

   recycled.

2. **Vocabulary** Explain the difference between evaporation and transpiration.

   Evaporation changes water from a liquid to a gas;

   transpiration is the evaporation of water from a plant's leaves.

3. **Reading Skill: Main Idea and Details** What process makes nitrogen usable by plants and animals? What are two ways this process takes place?

   nitrogen fixation; from lightning or the action of bacteria

   _____

4. **Critical Thinking: Analyze** Why is conserving fresh water important?

   It is scarce in some places.

5. **Inquiry Skill: Infer** The trees in a large area of tropical rain forest were removed. Infer how the water cycle and the surviving ecosystem could be affected. Explain your answer.

   Transpiration from leaves no longer adds water vapor to

   the air. This means less water will condense and fall as

   precipitation. The area may get drier.

Test Prep

Nitrogen gas in the air can be used by

A most plants.

B certain animals.

C certain bacteria.

D all organisms.

How Does Energy Cycle in Ecosystems?

1. Main Idea Explain how energy moves when one organism eats another.

Food contains energy. When one organism eats another, the

consumer gets energy from that organism.

2. Vocabulary What is the difference between a food web and an energy pyramid?

food web: shows food relationships within a community;

energy pyramid: shows energy between trophic levels

3. Reading Skill: Sequence Put the following organisms in the correct order in a food chain: grasshopper, grass, bird.

grass, grasshopper, bird

4. Critical Thinking: Synthesize Why do food chains stop at top-level consumers such as lions or bears?

There is not enough energy to support another trophic level

of organisms that would eat big carnivores.

5. Inquiry Skill: Use Models Diagram a food web that ends with a person who does not eat meat, but does eat animal products such as eggs, milk, and cheese. Food webs should start with the Sun and end with a person.

Test Prep

What do decomposers do?

A Eat bacteria and fungi.

B Produce oxygen.

C Break down dead plant and animal matter.

D Eat plants and other producers only.

Use with page B29

What Are Earth's Ecosystems?

1. **Main Idea** Explain how the abiotic factors in an ecosystem determine the types of organisms living there. Use a desert biome as an example.

   Organisms that live in a desert must survive abiotic factors

   of high temperatures and lack of water.

2. **Vocabulary** Define *biodiversity*. Explain which biome has the greatest biodiversity and why.

   Biodiversity is the variety of organisms in an area. Tropical

   rain forests have the greatest biodiversity because of the

   year-round warm temperatures and lots of rain.

3. **Reading Skill: Cause and Effect** Explain why different ocean zones are home to very different species.

   Each zone has different characteristics. The species in each

   zone are adapted to those characteristics.

4. **Critical Thinking: Evaluation** Based on the adaptations of animals, evaluate what might happen to the animals in a biome if Earth's temperature increased.

   Animals adapted to cold climates might have trouble

   surviving because they would be too warm.

5. **Inquiry Skill: Compare** (See page B45.)

   desert climate: high temperatures, little precipitation;

   tropical climate: warm temperatures, a lot of precipitation

Test Prep

Shrubs, lemmings, arctic foxes, and snowy owls are found in

A the taiga biome.

C the tundra biome.

B the tropical forest biome.

D the temperate forest biome.

Name _____   Date _____

What Roles Do Species Play?

1. **Main Idea** Explain how each species in an ecosystem depends on other species.

   They depend on other organisms for nutrients. If one

   species disappears, it can affect the entire system.

2. **Vocabulary** How is a carnivore different from an omnivore?

   Both will eat animals; an omnivore will also eat plants.

   _____

3. **Reading Skill: Classify** Classify each of the following species as producers, herbivores, carnivores, or omnivores: deer, raccoon, oak tree, rabbit, cactus, grass, rattlesnake.

   producers: oak tree, cactus, grass; herbivores: deer, rabbit;

   carnivore: rattlesnake; omnivore: raccoon

4. **Critical Thinking: Apply** Which of the following species would you expect to be most vulnerable to biomagnification: hawk, bumblebee, oak tree, deer, or raccoon? Explain your answer.

   hawk; it's at the top of the food chain.

5. **Inquiry Skill: Hypothesize** Create a hypothesis to predict what would happen to the lynx population if the hare population died off.

   The lynx population would decrease.

Test Prep

A niche is

A   a type of forest biome.

B   a type of tropical bird.

C   the part of a food web occupied by a top predator.

D   the specific role of a species in an ecosystem.

What Relationships Do Species Have?

1. Main Idea What is symbiosis?

Symbiosis is a close living relationship between species.

2. Vocabulary How is mutualism different from commensalism?

In mutualism, both species benefit. In commensalism, one

species benefits, and the other is unharmed.

3. Reading Skill: Classify Classify each of the following relationships as mutualism, commensalism, or parasitism: anemone and clownfish, robin and oak, alga and fungus, dog and tapeworm, tick and human.

anemone and clownfish: mutualism; robin and oak:

commensalism; alga and fungus: mutualism; dog and

tapeworm: parasitism; tick and human: parasitism

4. Critical Thinking: Synthesize Parasites make up only a small proportion of all species. Why do you think this is so? (Hint: Think about what would happen if most species were parasitic.)

With too many parasites, there wouldn't be enough hosts.

5. Inquiry Skill: Infer Suppose you discovered a new animal species that did not have a digestive system. What could you infer about how this species lives?

It is a parasite living in another organism's digestive system,

taking in food that has already been digested.

Test Prep

A lichen is an example of

A competition.

B mutualism.

C commensalism.

D parasitism.

What Limits Population Growth?

1. **Main Idea** What type of population will be most vulnerable to disease?

   one stressed by overcrowding or lack of food and water

2. **Vocabulary** Write a short paragraph using the terms *population growth* and *limiting factors*.

   Sample answer: Population growth is controlled by limiting

   factors such as food or space.

3. **Reading Skill: Cause and Effect** A species becomes extinct. Explain the possible causes for the extinction.

   habitat loss, disease, loss of food source, and increased

   number of predators

4. **Critical Thinking: Evaluate** A park ranger decides to open a brief hunting season for deer within a park. Why might the ranger have made this decision?

   Decreasing the deer population to the carrying capacity will

   help balance the ecosystem.

5. **Inquiry Skill: Predict** An invasive bird species enters an ecosystem and preys on its insects. How might this species change the ecosystem? Explain your reasoning.

   If the invaders destroy the insects, it could mean fewer

   native organisms that depend on insects.

Test Prep

Which of the following is NOT a limiting factor?

A disease

B competition

C predation

D extinction

What Are Biodiversity and Succession?

1. **Main Idea** What type of area will undergo the fastest ecological succession?

   an area that was recently disturbed and is in the early

   stages of secondary succession

2. **Vocabulary** Write a brief paragraph that explains why biodiversity is important.

   Sample answer: One species can get a disease and

   disappear without changing the whole ecosystem.

3. **Reading Skill: Compare and Contrast** Compare primary and secondary succession.

   primary: occurs on previously uninhabited land; secondary:

   occurs in damaged or destroyed ecosystems

4. **Critical Thinking: Apply** Sea lampreys reduced lake trout populations in the Great Lakes. How is this invader similar to the Chinese snakehead?

   Neither had natural predators to control the population.

5. **Inquiry Skill: Experiment** Write a procedure for investigating insect biodiversity on your school campus.

   Procedures should demonstrate an understanding of the

   principles of biodiversity.

Test Prep

Which statement correctly describes a biodiversity hotspot?

A places where the greatest numbers of plant and animal species are threatened

B places where the ecosystems are most out of balance

C places where the most species have become extinct

D places near volcanoes

What Are Properties of Minerals?

1. **Main Idea** List the physical properties of a mineral that can be determined by observation.

   crystal shape, luster, color

2. **Vocabulary** Write a short paragraph using the terms *mineral* and *luster*.

   Sample answer: One physical property of minerals is luster.

   Some minerals have a metallic luster, which is shiny. Other

   minerals may have a dull, pearly, or silky luster.

3. **Reading Skill: Categorize** Explain how the physical property of hardness is used to categorize minerals.

   Minerals can be categorized in order of hardness on the

   Mohs scale.

4. **Critical Thinking: Apply** Some industrial saw blades are coated with small particles of diamond. Explain why this might be useful and what might happen if another mineral was used.

   Diamond is used because it is the hardest mineral. Other hard

   minerals will not be able to cut through as many materials.

5. **Inquiry Skill: Use Numbers** An unknown mineral scratches a penny, which has a hardness of 3 on the Mohs scale. A knife blade with a hardness of 5 scratches the mineral. What is the hardness of the mineral?

   within the range of just over 3 to just under 5

Test Prep

Which physical property can be determined by rubbing a mineral across a rough tile?

A streak

B luster

C hardness

D cleavage

Use with page C11

What Are the Three Classes of Rock?

1. Main Idea Describe how igneous rocks are formed.

They form as magma cools and minerals crystallize.

2. Vocabulary Write a brief paragraph using the phrases *sedimentary rock*, *metamorphic rock*, and *rock cycle*.

Sample answer: The rock cycle is a process during which a

type of rock is transformed into another type. For example,

sedimentary rock becomes metamorphic rock.

3. Reading Skill: Compare and Contrast Compare and contrast the steps in the formation of igneous rocks with large crystals and igneous rocks with small crystals.

Both are formed when magma reaches Earth's surface and

cools. If cooled quickly, the result is small crystals. If cooled

slowly, the result is large crystals.

4. Critical Thinking: Analyze A rock formation has layers of shale and limestone. What can be inferred about the changes that the landscape has gone through?

The area where the rock originally formed was underwater

and at a much lower elevation. The region must have been

pushed up over time.

5. Inquiry Skill: Observe (See page C25.)

It is probably a sedimentary rock.

Test Prep

Which of these rocks formed from magma as it cooled and hardened?

A shale

B marble

C granite

D limestone

What Do Rocks and Fossils Reveal?

1. **Main Idea** How can fossils tell us about how Earth's climate has changed over time?

   We can infer what the climate was when the fossil organism

   was alive and compare it with today's climate.

2. **Vocabulary** Write a paragraph describing how fossils are formed. Include an example.

   Fossils are formed when once-living organisms become

   buried in sediment that forms sedimentary rock.

3. **Reading Skill: Text Structure** Write a paragraph describing the evidence for continental drift. Underline the sentence that contains the main idea.

   Students should list and describe the four main pieces of

   evidence for continental drift.

4. **Critical Thinking: Evaluate** What would you say to someone who claimed that continents never move, because they are now exactly where they were hundreds of years ago?

   Hundreds of years is not enough time for continents to

   have moved much (though they have moved a little).

5. **Inquiry Skill: Infer** (See page C39.)

   The backyard was once under water.

Test Prep

What would be proved by the discovery of a fish fossil in the uppermost layer of a sample of sedimentary rock?

A Fish once lived on dry land.

B The fish lived at a later time than fossils from layers below.

C The fish lived in a warm area.

D The fish lacked hard parts.

What Are Tectonic Plates?

1. Main Idea What is the mechanism that causes tectonic plates to move on Earth's surface?

a combination of mantle convection and slab pull

2. Vocabulary Write a sentence using the terms *lithosphere* and *crust*.

Sample answer: The lithosphere is made up of Earth's crust

and the top part of the mantle.

3. Reading Skill: Main Idea and Details In one or two sentences, summarize the main idea of the *Sea-Floor Spreading* section.

Scientists discovered rift valleys on the floor of the world's

oceans where sea-floor spreading occurs. By studying

sea-floor spreading, scientists were able to learn much

about the mechanisms of plate tectonics.

4. Critical Thinking: Synthesis What role did sea-floor spreading play in arranging the continents as they are today?

Sea-floor spreading created the great ocean basins that lie

between many continents today.

5. Inquiry Skill: Use Models Describe how you would create a model of sea-floor spreading, using everyday materials.

Answers will vary, but should support the ideas

behind the process of sea-floor spreading.

Test Prep

Which layer of Earth is solid and rocky?

A outer core

B lithosphere

C mantle

D inner core

What Changes Do Moving Plates Cause?

1. **Main Idea** What geologic events are likely to be found at convergent plate boundaries?

   mountain chains, volcanoes, and volcanic island chains

2. **Vocabulary** Write a sentence using the terms *focus* and *epicenter*.

   Sample answer: The focus of an earthquake is where

   movement first occurs; the epicenter is above the focus.

3. **Reading Skill: Cause and Effect** Explain what causes earthquakes, and how earthquakes affect the land, buildings, and people.

   Earthquakes occur when stress builds up between moving

   plates. Seismic waves collapse structures, hurting people.

4. **Critical Thinking: Synthesis** Iceland is on an island that is located on top of a divergent boundary in the Atlantic Ocean. List the types of geologic activity you would expect to see there, and suggest some changes you would expect the island to experience in the future.

   volcanic activity, earthquakes, movement at plate boundary;

   The island may widen as the plates continue to move.

5. **Inquiry Skill: Use Models** (See page C59.)

   Answers will vary, but should demonstrate an understanding

   of the principles of a working seismograph.

Test Prep

Which of these geologic features would you expect to find at a transform fault boundary?

A active volcanoes   C faults

B a mountain chain   D hydrothermal vents

Why Are Fossil Fuels Limited?

1. **Main Idea** Describe fossil fuel formation. Where are the fuels found?

   They are formed from organisms' remains. Heat and

   pressure cause the remains to change metamorphically.

2. **Vocabulary** Write a paragraph using the terms *nonrenewable resource* and *fossil fuels*. Explain why fossil fuels should be used wisely.

   Sample answer: Fossil fuels are nonrenewable resources

   because they take millions of years to form. They cannot be

   replaced easily, so they should be used wisely.

3. **Reading Skill: Problem-Solution** What are two ways people have begun to solve the problem of pollution?

   strict laws and better technology

4. **Critical Thinking: Evaluation** What are some advantages and disadvantages of burning fossil fuels for their energy? Why are scientists researching new energy sources?

   Fossil fuels provide an excellent source to fulfill our energy

   needs. However, they are nonrenewable resources and

   burning them makes air pollution. Scientists are researching

   new energy sources to reduce our dependence on them.

5. **Inquiry Skill: Use Numbers** (See page C73.) Students' graphs should show values for how much energy each type of light bulb produces along one axis and the names of the bulbs along the other axis.

Test Prep

Which of these fossil fuels is used to make gasoline?

A natural gas   **B** bituminous coal   **C** petroleum   **D** peat

How Can Renewable Energy Be Used?

1. **Main Idea** Describe some ways that renewable energy resources can be used to power automobiles.

   Hydrogen fuel cells release energy with no harmful

   byproducts. Electricity fuels cars using rechargeable batteries.

2. **Vocabulary** Define the term *hydroelectric energy*. Describe how this kind of energy is made.

   Hydroelectric energy is electric energy generated from

   moving water. Moving water turns turbines. The mechanical

   energy is converted into electric energy.

3. **Reading Skill: Main Idea and Details** What is biomass and why is it a renewable energy resource?

   It is once-living matter with stored solar energy. It is

   renewed as organisms die and give off waste.

4. **Critical Thinking: Evaluation** What would you say to someone who said that the United States should switch from fossil fuels to nuclear energy?

   Sample answer: Fossil fuels are limited, and nuclear energy

   is not. Burning fossil fuels creates pollution, but nuclear

   reactions create radioactive waste.

5. **Inquiry Skill: Use Models** (See page C88.)

   Sample answer: a simple pinwheel

Test Prep

What uses heat from Earth to make electricity?

A solar cells

B hydroelectric dams

C geothermal plants

D hydrogen fuel cells

Why Does Weather Occur?

1. **Main Idea** What is an air mass?

   a body of air with similar temperature and water vapor

   throughout

2. **Vocabulary** Write a short paragraph using the terms *air mass*, *front*, and *precipitation*.

   Sample answer: Two air masses that meet along a front have

   different temperatures and pressure. These differences often

   cause precipitation.

3. **Reading Skill: Compare and Contrast** How do cumulus clouds and stratus clouds compare?

   Both are formed from water droplets. Cumulus clouds look

   puffy, and stratus clouds look layered.

4. **Critical Thinking: Synthesis** What would you conclude about the weather if the barometric pressure was dropping and you could see cumulonimbus clouds in the sky?

   You would expect rain followed by cooler temperatures.

5. **Inquiry Skill: Record Data** Make a chart to record these data: the boiling point of water on a flat ocean beach is 100°C (212°F). The boiling point of water on a mountain 1,500 m above sea level is 95°C (203°F). Infer the boiling point of water at 3,000 m above sea level. 0, 100°C; 1,500, 95°C; 3,000, 90°C

Test Prep

In which layer of the atmosphere does most weather occur?

A troposphere

B stratosphere

C mesosphere

D exosphere

What Are Global Weather Patterns?

1. **Main Idea** How does the Coriolis effect change the direction of winds?

   It causes the paths of winds to curve.

2. **Vocabulary** Use the term *prevailing winds* to describe surface currents in the ocean.

   Prevailing winds blow in a particular direction and cause

   water at the ocean's surface to move in that direction.

3. **Reading Skill: Sequence** What is the sequence of events that results in an El Niño event?

   Prevailing winds weaken or die. Surface ocean currents

   reverse, so warm water moves eastward across the Pacific

   Ocean. Global weather patterns are altered.

4. **Critical Thinking: Apply** What might happen to atmospheric carbon dioxide levels if all countries switched to alternatives to fossil fuels?

   Carbon dioxide levels in the atmosphere would decline.

5. **Inquiry Skill: Infer** What do you think the temperature would be like on a planet that had an atmosphere rich in carbon dioxide?

   It would be hot.

Test Prep

Which property of carbon dioxide gas is important to the greenhouse effect?

A The gas reflects energy.

B The gas absorbs energy.

C The gas allows energy to pass through.

D The gas blocks the movement of energy.

How Can Storms Be Tracked?

1. **Main Idea** How do fronts cause thunderstorms to develop?

   Warm, moist air rises and forms cumulonimbus clouds.

   _____

2. **Vocabulary** Write a sentence using the terms *thunderstorm* and *tornado*.

   Sample answer: A tornado can develop during a severe

   thunderstorm.

3. **Reading Skill: Text Structure** What steps occur in the development of a hurricane?

   Hurricanes start as thunderstorms over warm, tropical

   oceans. The thunderstorms intensify and start rotating

   around the low-pressure zone, forming a hurricane.

4. **Critical Thinking: Analyze** Why are hurricanes referred to as powerful, while tornadoes are referred to as violent?

   Hurricanes cover a larger area and move slowly. Tornadoes

   can have higher wind speeds but don't last as long.

5. **Inquiry Skill: Predict** What will happen to a hurricane as it begins to move onto land?

   Hurricanes lose strength because they no longer have large

   amounts of water vapor to fuel cloud development.

Test Prep

A severe storm that forms quickly and has heavy rain and lightning is called a

A hurricane.

B thunderstorm.

C tornado.

D blizzard.

How Does the Sun Affect Earth?

1. Main Idea Explain why Earth has seasons.

Earth revolves around the Sun at a tilt. This affects the hours

of sunlight that areas receive throughout the year.

2. Vocabulary What is the difference between Earth's rotation and Earth's revolution?

Earth's rotation is the spinning of Earth on its axis. Earth's

revolution is the orbiting of Earth around the Sun.

3. Reading Skill: Text Structure List four ways the Sun affects Earth.

The Sun keeps Earth in orbit; it powers photosynthesis; it

lights Earth; it heats Earth.

4. Critical Thinking: Synthesis Use what you know about Earth's revolution to explain why a constellation might be seen in the summer sky, but not in winter.

In summer, you can see a constellation's position while your

hemisphere faces the Sun. By winter, Earth has orbited

halfway around the Sun. You then face away from the

constellation.

5. Inquiry Skill: Analyze Data (See page D51.)

It is spring (in the Northern Hemisphere.)

Test Prep

When would most locations on Earth experience 12 hours of daytime and 12 hours of nighttime?

A summer solstice

B fall equinox

C December

D May

How Do Eclipses Occur?

1. **Main Idea** Explain the difference between a solar eclipse and a lunar eclipse.

A solar eclipse occurs when the Moon is between the Sun

and Earth and the Moon's shadow falls on Earth. A lunar

eclipse occurs when Earth is between the Sun and Moon

and Earth's shadow falls on the Moon.

2. **Vocabulary** Use a diagram to help define the terms *umbra* and *penumbra*. umbra: darker, central region of Earth's shadow; penumbra: fainter region that surrounds the umbra

3. **Reading Skill: Sequence** The word *wane* means "to decrease gradually in power or intensity." Sketch and label several waning Moon phases. Sample answer: full Moon, waning Moon, last quarter, crescent

4. **Critical Thinking: Analyze** Explain why you won't see the Moon at night during its new Moon phase.

The Moon is between the Sun and Earth. Its illuminated

side faces entirely away from Earth.

5. **Inquiry Skill: Infer** A transit of a certain planet is never visible from Earth. What can you infer about the orbit of that planet around the Sun?

It lies outside Earth's orbit.

Test Prep

What would you observe in a location where the Moon's penumbral shadow falls on Earth?

A a partial lunar eclipse

B a partial solar eclipse

C a planetary transit

D a full moon

What Causes Tides?

1. Main Idea What are tides and how are they caused?

Tides are the daily changes in the ocean level. They are

caused by the Moon's gravitational pull on oceans.

2. Vocabulary Write a paragraph using the terms *tidal range*, *spring tides*, and *neap tides*.

Sample answer: The tidal range is greater during spring

tides than during neap tides.

3. Reading Skill: Cause and Effect An area experiences extra-high tides and extra-low tides. What causes this?

The Sun and Moon are aligned, so they pull the ocean water

more strongly.

4. Critical Thinking: Apply The Moon's mass is about 1.2 percent of Earth's mass. If the Moon were less massive, what would the effect be on Earth's tidal bulges?

The Moon's gravitational pull would be weaker, and Earth's

tidal bulges would be smaller.

5. Inquiry Skill: Compare Is the difference between high and low tides greater for spring tides or neap tides? Explain.

The difference is greater for spring tides, because they

result from the pull of both the Moon and the Sun.

Test Prep

Tides that are receding from high tide to low tide are

A ebb tides.

B flood tides.

C spring tides.

D neap tides.

Use with page D67

How Do Scientists Study the Planets?

1. Main Idea What types of objects are in orbit around the Sun?

planets, asteroids, comets

2. Vocabulary Define the term *astronomical unit*.

average distance of Earth from the Sun, or 150 million km

3. Reading Skill: Draw Conclusions Which planets were probably formed under similar conditions?

similar: Mercury, Venus, Earth, Mars; similar: Jupiter, Saturn,

Neptune, Uranus

4. Critical Thinking: Evaluate Pluto has an irregular orbit that sometimes brings it inside the orbit of Neptune. Do you think this does or does not support the theory that Pluto was once a moon of Neptune? Explain your answer.

Accept any well-reasoned response.

5. Inquiry Skill: Use Models If you were making a paper model of the solar system, how would you represent comets, meteoroids, and asteroids?

Most asteroids should be orbiting between Mars and Jupiter,

and some comets should be orbiting beyond Neptune.

Meteoroids should be shown bumped out of orbiting paths.

Test Prep

Venus is similar to Earth because

A it has liquid water on its surface.

B it has surface features that are like those on Earth.

C the temperature is about the same.

D the length of its day is about 24 hours.

What Have Scientists Learned About Stars?

1. **Main Idea** Why are different types of telescopes used to observe and study stars?

   They study different properties of space objects.

2. **Vocabulary** Compare black holes and neutron stars.

   Both are the final stages in the life cycle of a massive star.

3. **Reading Skill: Categorize or Classify** How are stars arranged on the Hertzsprung-Russell diagram?

   by absolute magnitude and temperature

4. **Critical Thinking: Apply** Where in its life cycle is our Sun? What will happen to the Sun for the remainder of its life?

   It is a main-sequence star. It will become a red giant and

   then a white dwarf.

5. **Inquiry Skill: Compare** Compare the three main types of galaxies.

   All are collections of gas, dust, and stars.

Test Prep

Which of these correctly sequences the stages in the life cycle of a massive star before becoming a supernova?

A nebula, protostar, main-sequence star, red supergiant

B neutron star, black hole, white dwarf

C red giant, black hole, neutron star

D protostar, planetary nebula, neutron star

Use with page D96

What Are Building Blocks of Matter?

1. **Main Idea** Where are protons, neutrons, and electrons found in an atom?

   Protons and neutrons are found in the nucleus. Electrons
   are found in the large area outside the nucleus.

2. **Vocabulary** Write a sentence using the terms *electron*, *ion*, and *proton*.

   Sample answer: A positive ion has fewer electrons than
   protons.

3. **Reading Skill: Main Idea** How did Rutherford's work help form the present-day model of the atom?

   Rutherford devised the theory that an atom has a positive
   nucleus surrounded by negative electrons.

4. **Critical Thinking: Synthesis** Copper, silver, and gold are located in the same group in the periodic table. What can you infer about these elements?

   They all have similar properties.

5. **Inquiry Skill: Use Numbers** (See page E15.)

Element	Protons	Neutrons	Electrons
C-13	6	7	6
Li-7	3	4	2
Cl-35	17	18	16

Test Prep

The elements are arranged in the periodic table according to what property?

A atomic mass

B atomic number

C density

D radioactivity

Use with page E15

What Is a Compound?

1. **Main Idea** How can matter be classified?

   as a pure substance or a mixture

2. **Vocabulary** Write a sentence that shows how the terms
   compound, *chemical bond*, and *molecule* are related.

   Sample answer: A compound is a pure substance made up

   of two or more elements held together by chemical bonds

   that form a molecule.

3. **Reading Skill: Text Structure** Use the text structure to
   describe how the sugars found in strawberries are classified.

   Strawberries contain fructose. Fructose is a carbohydrate,

   which is a carbon compound.

4. **Critical Thinking: Apply** The chemical formula for the
   compound water is H_2O. How does water's chemical formula
   relate to the numbers and kinds of atoms in its molecules?

   There are 2 hydrogen atoms bonded to 1 oxygen atom.

5. **Inquiry Skill: Compare** How is methane (found in natural gas)
   similar to gasoline (the fuel used in most cars)?

   Methane is a hydrocarbon, and gasoline is a mixture of

   hydrocarbons.

Test Prep

A molecule of formaladehyde contains one carbon atom, two
hydrogen atoms, and one oxygen atom. What is the chemical
formula for formaldehyde?

A 2CHO

B C_2HO

C CH_2O

D C_2H_2O

What Properties Do Solutions Have?

1. **Main Idea** Describe some homogeneous mixtures.

   Some homogeneous mixtures are solutions. A solution is

   made up of a solute and a solvent.

2. **Vocabulary** How do homogeneous and heterogeneous mixtures differ?

   Homogeneous mixtures are evenly mixed, and you cannot

   distinguish different types of matter that compose them.

   Heterogeneous mixtures are unevenly mixed, and you can

   often see the different components.

3. **Reading Skill: Draw Conclusions** A mixture of water molecules, sodium ions, and chlorine ions is uniform. Is the mixture heterogeneous or homogeneous? Explain.

   The mixture is homogeneous. It is evenly mixed.

4. **Critical Thinking: Apply** To make broth, Amy dissolves a bouillon cube in one cup of water. How might she make the bouillon dissolve quickly?

   She could stir the bouillon while she heated it.

5. **Inquiry Skill: Record Data** The table in your book shows the amounts of each salt that can be dissolved in 100 g of water at 20°C. Make a bar graph to compare the data. Students' bar graphs should accurately display the table data.

Test Prep

Which is a type of alloy?

A salt water

B pure gold

C vegetable soup

D bronze

What Are Acids and Bases?

1. **Main Idea** List some properties of acids and bases.

   Acids taste sour and turn blue litmus paper red. Bases feel

   slippery, taste bitter, and turn red litmus paper blue.

2. **Vocabulary** Describe acids and bases in terms of pH and hydrogen ions.

   An acid has a low pH, which means a high concentration of

   hydrogen ions. A base has a high pH, which means a low

   concentration of hydrogen ions.

3. **Reading Skill: Compare and Contrast** How does the pH of an acid compare with the pH of a neutral solution?

   The pH of an acid is lower than the pH of water, which is 7,

   or neutral.

4. **Critical Thinking: Analyze** Would a substance with a high pH turn litmus paper red or blue? Explain your answer.

   It turns red litmus paper blue because it is a base.

5. **Inquiry Skill: Classify** A gardener discovers that her prize hydrangeas have turned from pink to blue. What can you say about the soil in which the flowers are growing?

   The soil once had a high pH but now has a low pH.

   _____

Test Prep

Vinegar contains acetic acid. What color will litmus paper turn in vinegar?

A blue

B red

C purple

D orange

What Is Physical Change?

1. **Main Idea** How is temperature related to the speed of particles in a substance?

   When temperature increases, average speed increases.

2. **Vocabulary** Compare and contrast the terms *temperature* and *thermal energy*.

   Temperature is a measurement of the average kinetic

   energy of a substance. Thermal energy is the total thermal

   energy of a substance.

3. **Reading Skill: Cause and Effect** What happens to the volume of a gas when its temperature decreases if the pressure is held constant?

   The volume of a gas decreases.

4. **Critical Thinking: Analyze** The temperature of a solid increases steadily for 10 minutes, remains 0°C for 3 minutes, and then increases again. The final sample is a liquid. What conclusion can you draw?

   The solid underwent a state change at 0°C.

5. **Inquiry Skill: Hypothesize** (See page E55.)

   It was warmer outside than inside. The increased temperature

   caused the volume of air particles inside the balloons to

   exceed maximum capacity.

Test Prep

Most substances increase in volume when temperature increases. What term describes this effect?

A thermal expansion

B melting point

C freezing point

D absolute temperature

Use with page E55

What Is Chemical Change?

1. **Main Idea** How is energy involved in a chemical change?

   Chemical changes involve breaking and forming of bonds.

   Energy is needed to do both.

2. **Vocabulary** How do endothermic and exothermic reactions differ?

   An endothermic reaction absorbs energy, while an exothermic

   reaction releases energy.

3. **Reading Skill: Main Idea and Details** During a chemical reaction, how do the substances that form differ from the substances that react?

   The substances that form have different properties and

   compositions than the substances that react.

4. **Critical Thinking: Apply** A chemical reaction in a lightstick causes it to give off a glowing green light. Explain why the reaction is endothermic or exothermic.

   exothermic; It releases energy in the form of light.

5. **Inquiry Skill: Observe** What kinds of observations can you make that might indicate a chemical change is taking place?

   change in color, production of heat, light, or sound

Test Prep

Which of the following is a chemical change?

A   liquid water freezing to form ice

B   electrolysis of water to form hydrogen and oxygen

C   salt dissolving in water to form a solution

D   separation of water from a salt solution through evaporation

Use with page E65

What Are Types of Chemical Reactions?

1. **Main Idea** What are five types of chemical reactions?

   synthesis, decomposition, single-replacement, double-

   replacement, combustion

2. **Vocabulary** How are balanced chemical equations related to the law of conservation of matter?

   Balanced chemical equations show that the numbers and

   types of atoms are the same on both sides.

3. **Reading Skill: Classify** What type of chemical reaction is represented by the following chemical equation?
   $2Na + Cl_2 \longrightarrow 2NaCl$

   The formation of sodium chloride from sodium and chlorine

   is a synthesis reaction.

4. **Critical Thinking: Apply** The chemical equation describing the burning of hydrogen gas is: $2H_2 + O_2 \longrightarrow 2H_2O$. Why is this both a synthesis and a combustion reaction?

   It is a synthesis reaction because two substances react

   to form a single substance. It is a combustion reaction

   because a substance reacts with oxygen to form water.

5. **Inquiry Skill: Compare** (See page E72.)

   The right side of the equation has more atoms. The

   balanced equation is: $Zn + 2HCl \longrightarrow ZnCl_2 + H_2$

Test Prep

What kind of reaction is described by the following equation?
$3CuCl_2 + 2Al \longrightarrow 2AlCl_3 + 3Cu$

A synthesis

C single-replacement

B decomposition

D double-replacement

What Is Conservation of Energy?

1. **Main Idea** Describe some properties of energy.

   Energy can't be created or destroyed, it can be transformed

   from one kind to another, and it can be potential or kinetic.

2. **Vocabulary** Explain the difference between potential energy and kinetic energy. Give an example of how one can be transformed into the other.

   potential: stored energy; kinetic: energy of motion; A

   person at the top of a cliff has potential energy, which

   becomes kinetic energy when she moves down the cliff.

3. **Reading Skill: Draw Conclusions** Describe how Earth would be affected if it no longer got energy from the Sun.

   Earth would not be warm enough to live on. Plants would

   not grow, and we would have nothing to eat.

4. **Critical Thinking: Analyze** A kitchen blender transforms electrical energy into mechanical energy. Why is the amount of mechanical energy produced less than the amount of electrical energy used?

   The blender loses energy from friction.

5. **Inquiry Skill: Compare** Nuclear fusion and nuclear fission both release huge amounts of energy. How are the two processes different?

   In fusion, small nuclei join together, while fission involves

   splitting nuclei.

Test Prep

Which of the following can be described as kinetic energy?

A chemical energy   **C** elastic energy

B gravitational energy   **D** mechanical energy

Use with page F11

How Do Waves Transfer Energy?

1. Main Idea Give two examples of how waves transmit energy.

Waves transmit energy through water or air.

2. Vocabulary Compare a longitudinal wave and a transverse wave. Give one example of each kind of wave.

longitudinal: back and forth, example: sound wave; transvers:

move up and down, example: electromagnetic wave.

3. Reading Skill: Sequence Describe why a sound seems to increase in pitch when its source moves toward a listener.

The movement gives the sound waves a boost in frequency

and makes them sound louder and higher pitched.

4. Critical Thinking: Apply A car is traveling quickly past a non-moving police car. The police siren is blaring loudly. Does the Doppler effect apply? Explain.

Yes, because the sound is moving in relation to the listener.

5. Inquiry Skill: Record Data Make a chart to record these data: a 20-km/h wind causes ocean waves 0.3 m high and 10 m long, a 30-km/h wind causes waves 0.8 m high and 22 m long, and a 40-km/h wind causes waves 1.6 m high and 38 m long.

Wind Speed	Amplitude	Wavelength
20 km/h	0.3 m	10 m
30 km/h	0.8 m	22 m
40 km/h	1.6 m	38 m

Test Prep

Which is an example of waves that can travel through empty space?

A sound waves   **C** longitudinal waves

B light waves   **D** seismic waves

Use with page F19

How Is Thermal Energy Transferred?

1. **Main Idea** Explain the relationship between particles in a substance and the substance's thermal energy.

   The faster particles move, the higher their thermal energy.

2. **Vocabulary** Use *thermal equilibrium* to describe what happens when a warm object touches a colder object.

   A warm object will transfer thermal energy to a cooler

   object, causing both to reach thermal equilibrium.

3. **Reading Skill: Text Structure** How do conduction, convection, and radiation transform thermal energy?

   Conduction transfers kinetic energy to cooler particles

   when two solids touch each other. Convection transfers

   thermal energy between liquids and gases. Radiation raises

   the kinetic energy of the object that intercepts it.

4. **Critical Thinking: Infer** A few days after a snowstorm, the roof of one house is still covered with snow, but the roof of another house is bare. What can you infer about the insulation under each roof? Explain.

   The roof with the snow is better insulated.

5. **Inquiry Skill: Communicate** (See page F29.) sketch: particles in the warm area moving more than particles in the cooler area

Test Prep

How is thermal energy transferred within an object?

A Tiny particles collide.

B Temperature is emitted from one particle to another.

C Heat flows from cooler particles to warmer particles.

D Conductor particles interact with insulator particles.

Use with page F29

What Is the Electromagnetic Spectrum?

1. Main Idea Describe the electromagnetic spectrum.

It organizes radiation according to energy level.

2. Vocabulary Write a paragraph that explains the differences between incandescent, fluorescent, and laser light.

Incandescent: created by glowing objects; fluorescent:

created by vapor that produces photons that hit phosphor,

which emits light; laser: coherent, single color

3. Reading Skill: Main Idea and Details Explain how atoms can be made to emit light.

When energy is added to an atom, electrons reach an excited

state. When they return to normal, they emit light energy.

4. Critical Thinking: Infer Why does coherent light need to be all of one color?

If it had waves with different wavelengths, the waves' crests

and troughs would not line up.

5. Inquiry Skill: Predict Scientists continue to study electomagnetic radiation from space. Do you think this radiation may provide evidence of intelligent life on other plantes? Explain your predictions.

Students' predictions will vary.

_____

Test Prep

Which type of electromagnetic radiation carries the most energy?

A radio waves   C x-rays

B visible light   D gamma rays

How Does Light Interact With Matter?

1. **Main Idea** Explain how light behaves when it interacts with different materials. Give examples.

   Light rays are reflected by shiny materials, such as metals, absorbed by dull materials, such as a black driveway, and transmitted by clear materials, such as windows.

2. **Vocabulary** Compare transparent and translucent objects.

   Transparent materials let most light rays through, while translucent materials let some light through.

3. **Reading Skill: Problem-Solution** The type on a written contract is too small to read with the naked eye. What could you use to read this contract? Explain.

   A convex lens; This type of lens can produce an image that is enlarged.

4. **Critical Thinking: Apply** You want to use a mirror to reflect a beam of light at right angles around a corner. What type of mirror would you use? Draw a diagram. A plane mirror; When placed at the desired angle, the light will reflect off the mirror at that angle.

5. **Inquiry Skill: Infer** When you shine a light on Object A, you see the light on the wall behind you. When you shine a light on Object B, you see the light on the wall behind Object B. What can you infer about Object A? What can you infer about Object B?

   Object A reflects light. Object B lets light through.

Test Prep

The bending of light as it enters a material is called

A absorption.

B reflection.

C refraction.

D illumination.

199

Use with page F61

What Are Static and Current Electricity?

1. **Main Idea** What is the difference between static electricity and current electricity?

   Static electricity is isolated electric charges in objects;

   current electricity is continuous flow of charges.

2. **Vocabulary** Write a short paragraph about electrical current using the terms *conductor* and *insulator*.

   Sample answer: Electric current passes easily through a

   conductor and is stopped by an insulator.

3. **Reading Skill: Compare and Contrast** How are direct current and alternating current alike? How are they different?

   Electrons flow from one point to another in both. DC current flows in only

   one direction, but AC current flows back and forth through a circuit.

4. **Critical Thinking: Synthesize** Is it possible for a circuit to be connected both in series and in parallel? Explain.

   Yes; In parts of the circuit, resistors may be in series, and in

   others, they may be in parallel.

5. **Inquiry Skill: Use Variables** (See page 77.)

   Designs should attempt to control variables.

Test Prep

Which statement describes the electrostatic force between two charged objects?

A It is greater when two objects are farther apart.

B It is greater if two objects have the same charge.

C It is greater when the charges of the objects are greater.

D It is zero if the charges of the objects repel one another.

How Are Electricity and Magnetism Related?

1. **Main Idea** How are electricity and magnetism related?

   An electric current can produce a magnetic field, and a

   magnetic field can produce an electric current.

2. **Vocabulary** Write a paragraph using the terms *electric generator* and *electric motor*.

   Sample answer: An electric motor is a device that converts

   electric energy into mechanical energy. This is the opposite

   of what an electric generator does.

3. **Reading Skill: Draw Conclusions** An electric motor and a generator are very similar in construction. Why is this so?

   They both need magnets, spinning parts, and wires.

4. **Critical Thinking: Analyze** What advantage does an AC motor provide over a DC motor?

   An AC motor does not require a commutator.

5. **Inquiry Skill: Hypothesize** Why does the armature of an electric motor rotate only in one direction?

   due to a pattern of attraction and repulsion between poles of

   the electromagnet and poles of the permanent magnet

Test Prep

An electric generator

A changes mechanical energy to electrical energy.

B changes electrical energy to mechanical energy.

C is powered by alternating current.

D changes sound waves to electric impulses.

Use with page F89

What Are Speed, Velocity, and Acceleration?

1. **Main Idea** How is speed measured? Include example of units of speed.

   Speed is calculated by dividing distance by time. Examples

   of units of speed include mi/h, km/h, and m/s.

2. **Vocabulary** Explain how *speed*, *velocity*, and *acceleration* are related to each other.

   All three describe an object's motion.

3. **Reading Skill: Problem-Solution** If a sprinter runs a distance of 100 m in 10 s, what is the sprinter's average speed?

   The sprinter's average speed is 10 m/s.

4. **Critical Thinking: Analyze** You are running east at a speed of 15 km/h. A car passes you traveling east at a speed of 50 km/h. You stop to wait for a bus and another car traveling east at a speed of 50 km/h passes you. How does your changing frame of reference affect how fast you observe each car as traveling?

   The second car will seem faster than the first car.

5. **Inquiry Skill: Predict** How will punching a hole in a parachute affect the rate at which it falls?

   It will fall faster.

Test Prep

Which describes velocity?

A 10 km per second

B 20 mi per hour

C 3 m per second, due east

D 15 cm along a ruler

202

Use with page F103

What Are Newton's Laws?

1. **Main Idea** Explain how force, mass, and acceleration are related.

   force = mass × acceleration
   _____

2. **Vocabulary** Use the terms *inertia* and *force* to describe Newton's first law of motion.

   Newton's first law states that force can be used to overcome
   _____

   inertia.
   _____

3. **Reading Skill: Main Idea** How do distance and mass affect the force of gravity?

   The force of gravity between two objects increases as their
   _____

   mass increases and decreases as the distance between
   _____

   them increases.
   _____

4. **Critical Thinking: Analyze** Many highways with steep hills have ramps for trucks that are moving too quickly. Why would trucks have a harder time than cars slowing down on steep hills?

   A large mass has more inertia than a small mass does.
   _____

5. **Inquiry Skill: Experiment** You have a board, wood blocks, and a toy car. Your goal is to build a ramp that sends the car as far across the floor as possible. What angle between the board and floor would be best? Design an experiment to find out.

   Designs should include systematically changing the slope
   _____

   angle and holding other factors constant.
   _____

Test Prep

Action and reaction forces

A prevent motion.

B are unbalanced forces.

C each act on a different object.

D each act in the same direction.

Why Do Machines Help Make Tasks Easier?

1. **Main Idea** Explain how simple machines can make tasks easier.

They change the size or direction of the force applied.

2. **Vocabulary** Why is the efficiency of a machine always less than 100 percent?

Friction decreases the efficiency.

3. **Reading Skill: Cause and Effect** How does a large steering wheel make it easier to turn a school bus?

The larger the steering wheel, the greater the distance it has to be turned, but less force is required to turn it.

4. **Critical Thinking: Apply** Piano movers sometimes move pianos up stairs, into trucks, and even through windows of tall buildings. Describe how simple machines can help them. Give at least three examples.

Wheels under the piano could help move it across flat surfaces. A pulley could lift it up a tall building. A ramp could help lift it from the street into a truck.

5. **Inquiry Skill: Hypothesize** (See page F128.)

Sample answer: The applied force increases with the mass of the rope. To test the hypothesis, measure the applied force for different masses of rope in the pulley

Test Prep

Mechanical advantage is

A the amount by which a machine multiplies force.

B the amount of force applied to a machine.

C the complexity of a machine.

D the amount of resistance force working against a machine.

Use with page F128

Ratio and Percent

Algae produce much of the oxygen that we breathe! There are about 18,900 different species of algae. Of these, 7,500 species are green algae, 6,000 species are yellow algae, 3,900 species are red algae, and 1,500 species are brown algae.

1. What percent of these species are green algae?

   40%
   _____

2. What percent of these species are yellow algae?

   32%
   _____

3. What percent of these species are red algae?

   20%
   _____

4. What percent of these species are brown algae?

   8%
   _____

5. Make a pie graph to show these data.

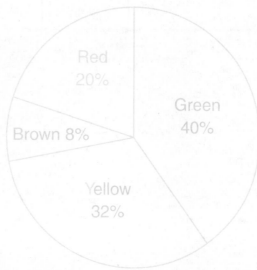

Algae Families
Distribution by Colors

Make a Table

Every cell in an organism needs energy. Most of the energy inside a cell is stored in molecules called ATPs. An ATP molecule acts like a tiny battery. Each cell needs many battery-like ATP molecules. For example, a typical *E. coli* cell needs about 2 million ATP molecules every second to survive!

1. How many ATP molecules does a typical *E. coli* cell need every minute?

   2 million × 60 = 120 million

2. How many ATP molecules does this *E. coli* cell need every 20 minutes?

   120 million × 20 = 2,400 millions = 2.4 billion

3. Complete the table below. Show how many ATP molecules a single cell would need in 2 hours.

2 hours

Time in minutes	20	40	60	80	100	120
ATPs in billions	2.4	4.8	7.2	9.6	12.0	14.4

Use with page A49

Probability

You can use a Punnett square to show the possible combinations of alleles in offspring. You can then find the probability of any combination.

Example: Rabbit 1 has gray fur, *G* and *g*.
Rabbit 2 has gray fur, *G* and *g*.
What are the possible outcomes for the color of their offspring's fur?
Possible outcomes: *GG*, *Gg*, *gG*, and *gg*

The probability of *GG* is 1 out of 4 or $\frac{1}{4}$.

The probability of *Gg* is 2 out of 4 or $\frac{1}{2}$.

The probability of *gg* is 1 out of 4 or $\frac{1}{4}$.

Solve.

1. A woman has two X chromosomes. A man has an X chromosome and a Y chromosome. What is the probability that a couple will have a girl (XX)?

   2 out 4 or $\frac{1}{2}$.

2. What is the probability that a couple has a boy (XY)?

   2 out 4 or $\frac{1}{2}$.

3. The father in this family has free earlobes (*Ef*). The mother in this family has attached earlobes (*ff*). What is the probability that a child in this family will have free earlobes?
   Hint: List the possible outcomes first.

   possible outcomes: *Ef, ff, ff, ff.* The probability of having a

   child with free earlobes is 1 out of 4, or $\frac{1}{4}$. The probability

   of having a child with attached earlobes is 3 out 4, or $\frac{3}{4}$.

Use with page A97

Calculate the Percent of a Number

Tuberculosis is caused by a species of bacteria called *Mycobacterium tuberculosis*. Some drugs can kill these bacteria. However, the species has evolved, so some bacteria are now resistant to these drugs.

Worldwide, 1.7 billion people are infected by tuberculosis. Currently 9.9% of infected people have tuberculosis bacteria that are resistant to the leading drug used to treat the disease. A smaller number, 1.4%, have tuberculosis bacteria that are resistant to the two leading drugs.

1. How many people infected with tuberculosis worldwide cannot be treated with the leading drug?

$1{,}700{,}000{,}000 \times 9.9\% = 1{,}700{,}000{,}000 \times 0.099 =$

168,300,000 or about 168 million people

2. How many people infected with tuberculosis worldwide cannot be treated with the two leading drugs?

$1{,}700{,}000{,}000 \times 1.4\% = 1{,}700{,}000{,}000 \times 0.014 =$

23,800,000 or about 24 million people

3. What is the number of people with tuberculosis that can be effectively treated with the leading drug?

$1{,}700{,}000{,}000 \times (100\% - 9.9\%) = 1{,}700{,}000{,}000 \times$

$90.1\% = 1{,}700{,}000{,}000 \times 0.901 = 1{,}531{,}700{,}000$ or about

1.53 billion people

Name _____ Date _____

Computation with Percent

The energy pyramid below shows how energy flows from producers to consumers. Producers get energy from the Sun. Consumers get energy from producers or from other consumers.

Energy Pyramid

0.1% Energy	Vultures (Tertiary Consumers)	
1% Energy	Owls (Secondary Consumers)	
10% Energy	Voles (Primary Consumers)	
100% Energy	Producers	

You can calculate the amount of energy transferred to a consumer from a producer.

Example: If a producer has 5,000 calories of energy available, how many calories can a primary consumer obtain from the producer? Multiply 50,000 by 10%. **Hint:** First write 10% as a decimal. 10% = 0.1
$5,000 \times 0.1 = 500$ calories

Use data from the diagram. Solve.

1. If a producer has 2,000 calories available, how many calories can a primary consumer, such as a vole, obtain from the producer?

   $2,000 \times 0.1 = 200$ calories

2. If a producer has 4,000 calories available, how many calories can a secondary consumer, such as an owl, obtain from the producer?

   $4,000 \times 0.01 = 40$ calories

Use with page B28

Calculate the Mean

The table shows average monthly temperatures at two locations in Antarctica: McMurdo and Rothera Point.

Month	Average Monthly Temperatures	
	McMurdo (°C)	Rothera Point (°C)
January	−0.2	0.8
February	−6.3	−0.1
March	−14	−1.9
April	−17.4	−4.5
May	−19	−7.1
June	−19.1	−9.9
July	−21.7	−11.6
August	−22.8	−11.8
September	−20.8	−9.1
October	−15.5	−6.1
November	−6.7	−2.8
December	−0.8	0.1

Find the mean temperature (to the nearest tenth of a degree) at each location for each period of time.

1. January through March   McMurdo, −6.8°C; Rothera, −0.4°C

2. April through June   McMurdo, −18.5°C; Rothera, −7.2°C

3. July through September   McMurdo, −21.8°C; Rothera, −10.8°C

4. October through December   McMurdo, −7.7°C; Rothera, −2.9°C

Use with page B43

Use Data from a Double Line Graph

The predator-prey relationship is a limiting factor of populations.

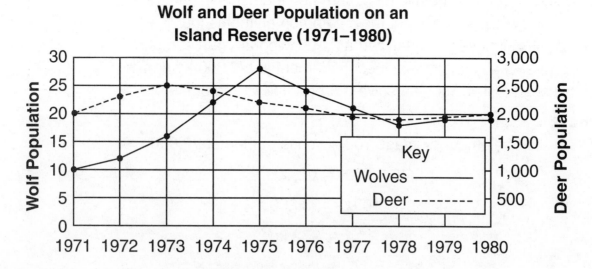

**Wolf and Deer Population on an
Island Reserve (1971–1980)**

Use the data from the graph above to answer the questions.

1. What does the scale on the *y*-axis on the left side show?

   the wolf population

2. What is the range of the data about the wolf population?

   10–28

3. What is the range of the data about the deer population?

   1,900–2,400

4. What does this graph show about the predator-prey relationship
   between wolves and deer?

   After the wolf population reaches a certain size, the deer

   population begins to decrease. If the deer population

   decreases too much, the wolf population also begins to

   decrease. You need a certain number of deer to sustain a

   certain number of wolves.

Name _____   Date _____

Solve Proportions

Earth's crust contains minerals. Minerals are made of elements. Oxygen and silicon are the two most common elements in minerals. The table below shows the eight most common elements found in Earth's crust. Suppose you analyzed a 2,000-kilogram (kg) sample of Earth's crust. What is the mass of each element in a 2,000-kg sample of Earth's crust? **Hint:** You can solve a proportion to find out.

Example:

% of element by mass/100 = mass of element/2,000

$46.6/100 = x/2,000$

$100x = 93,200$

$x = 932$ kg

Percentage of Some Chemical Elements in 2,000 kg of Earth's Crust

Element	Symbol	Percent (by mass)	Mass
Oxygen	O	46.60	932 kg
Silicon	Si	27.72	554.4 kg
Aluminum	Al	8.13	162.6 kg
Iron	Fe	5.00	100 kg
Calcium	Ca	3.63	72.6 kg
Sodium	Na	2.82	56.4 kg
Potassium	K	2.59	51.8 kg
Magnesium	Mg	2.09	41.8 kg

1. Use the data in the table to find the mass of each element in a 2,000-kg sample of Earth's crust. Place your answers in the correct row of the table.

Convert Units of Measurement

Earthquakes take place when rocks beneath Earth's surface move. The table below gives the depth of four earthquakes that took place in 2004.

Four Earthquakes of 2004

Date	Magnitude	Location	Depth (in km)
Mar 07	7.3	South Coast of Papua, Indonesia	10
July 25	7.3	Southern Sumatra, Indonesia	582
Dec 23	8.1	North of Macquarie Island	10
Dec 26	9.0	West Coast of Northern Sumatra	30

Example: The earthquake that occurred on March 7, 2004, was located 10 km beneath Earth's surface. How many feet is that? There are 3,333 feet in 1 kilometer. To convert kilometers to feet, you can use a ratio of kilometers to feet, 3,333. Then write a proportion and solve. Let f stand for the unknown number of feet.

$$\frac{1}{3,333} = \frac{10}{f}$$
$$f = 10 \times 3,333$$
$$f = 33,333$$

1. How many feet beneath the surface was the December 23 earthquake?

33,333 feet
_____

2. How many feet beneath the surface was the December 26 earthquake?

99,999 feet
_____

3. How many feet beneath the surface was the July 25 earthquake?

1,939,806 feet
_____

Decimal Multiplication

Petroleum oil is pumped from the ground and poured into barrels. The United States uses about 20 million barrels of petroleum oil every day. A barrel holds 42 gallons of oil. The oil in barrels is processed. The table shows the products that are obtained from processing petroleum oil.

1. About how many gallons of home heating oil are processed from 20 million barrels of petroleum oil?

   1.76 × 20 million = 35.2 million gallons

2. About how many gallons of gasoline are processed from 20 million barrels of petroleum oil each day?

   19.69 × 20 million = 393.8 million gallons

3. About how many gallons of gasoline are processed in one year?

   365 × 393.8 million = 143.7 billion gallons

4. Suppose that cars can travel an average of 25 miles on one gallon of gasoline. How many miles can people drive using all the gasoline refined in the United States in one year?

   25 × 143.7 billion = 3.6 trillion miles

**Products Refined from
One Barrel of Petroleum Oil**

Products	Quantities (in gallons)
Gasoline	19.69
Distillate Fuel Oil	9.70
Aviation Jet Fuel	4.03
Home Heating Oil	1.76
Still Gas	1.89
Petroleum Coke	2.14
Liquefied Refinery Gas	1.76
Asphalt and Road Oil	1.34
Feedstock Products	1.13
Lubricants	0.46
Kerosene	0.17
Miscellaneous Products	0.30
Waxes	0.04

Represent Data in Different Ways

The diagram shows how energy from the Sun is dispersed.

The Sun's Energy on Earth

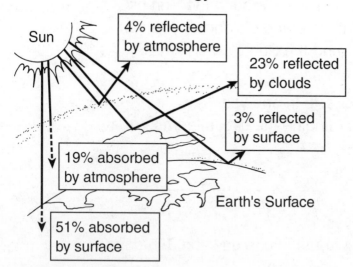

1. Chang made a pie chart to show these data. Label the parts of Chang's pie chart. Write what percent of the Sun's energy each segment represents.

Title: Sun's Energy on Earth

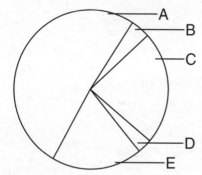

Key: A = 51% absorbed by surface

B = 4% reflected by atmosphere

C = 23% reflected by clouds

D = 3% reflected by surface

E = 19% absorbed by atmosphere

2. What total percent of the Sun's energy is reflected away from Earth?

4% + 23% + 3% = 30%

Use with page D15

Problem Solving Using Formulas

Earth revolves around the Sun. Earth makes one full turn around the Sun in about one year. The average distance between Earth and the Sun is 150 million kilometers. Earth travels around the Sun on an elliptical orbit. However, to calculate average distances, you can assume that Earth traces a circle around the Sun.

1. What is the distance traveled by Earth in one year?
   Hint: You can use the formula for finding the circumference of a circle: $C = 2\pi r$. ($\pi = 3.14$)

   $2 \times \pi \times 150$ million km $= 942$ million km

2. How many hours are there in a year?
   Hint: You know that there are 24 hours in one day and 365 days in one year.

   $24 \times 365 = 8{,}760$

3. At what speed is Earth traveling around the Sun?
   Hint: You can use the speed/time/distance formula, speed (s) = time (t)/distance (d).

   $942{,}000{,}000 / 8{,}760 = 107{,}534$ km/hr

4. A commercial jet, the Concorde, flew at about 2,200 km per hour. How many times faster is Earth going around the Sun than the Concorde flew through the sky?
   Hint: You can simplify a ratio that compares the speed of Earth to the speed of the Concorde.

   $107{,}534 / 2{,}200 = 48.9$ or about 50 times faster

Use with page D46–D48

Multiply with Millions

Scientists calculate distances in space with astronomical units (AU). One AU is equal to 150 million kilometers. The table shows the mean distance from the Sun of each planet, measured in astronomical units (AU). To find the average distance from the Sun in kilometers, you can multiply the distance given in AU by 150 million.

Example: To find the average distance from the Sun of Neptune, you can multiply the distance in AU by 150 million.

  30.1 × 150 million = 4,515 million or
  4 trillion 515 million km

Calculate the distance from the Sun for each planet given below. Use the data from the table.

Distances from the Sun

Planet	Mean Distance from the Sun (in AU)
Mercury	0.4
Venus	0.7
Earth	1
Mars	1.5
Jupiter	5.2
Saturn	9.5
Uranus	19.2
Neptune	30.1
Pluto	39.5

1. Mercury 0.4 × 150 million = 60 million km

2. Venus 0.7 × 150 million = 105 million km

3. Mars 1.5 × 150 million = 225 million km

4. Jupiter 5.2 × 150 million = 780 million km

5. Saturn 9.5 × 150 million = 1 trillion 425 million km

6. Uranus 19.2 × 150 million = 2 trillion 880 million km

7. Pluto 39.5 × 150 million = 5 trillion 925 million km

Use with page D83

Write Ratios

Chemical formulas show the number of atoms of each element in a substance. The table shows the chemical formulas for some everyday compounds.

Compound	Elements in This Compound	Chemical Formula
water	hydrogen and oxygen	H_2O
ascorbic acid (vitamin C)	carbon, hydrogen, and oxygen	$C_6H_8O_6$
caffeine	carbon, hydrogen, nitrogen, and oxygen	$C_8H_{10}N_4O_2$
saccharine	carbon, hydrogen, nitrogen, oxygen, and sulfur	$C_7H_5NO_3S$

Write each ratio using a:b.

1. What is the ratio of hydrogen atoms to oxygen atoms in water?

2:1

2. What is the ratio of hydrogen atoms to oxygen atoms in ascorbic acid?

8:6 or 4:3

3. What is the ratio of hydrogen atoms to nitrogen atoms in caffeine?

10:4 or 5:2

4. What is the ratio of hydrogen atoms to nitrogen atoms in saccharine?

5:1

Calculate a Percentage

The chemical formula of carbon dioxide is CO_2. It shows that one molecule of carbon dioxide contains one carbon atom and two oxygen atoms. You can find the percent of carbon atoms and the percent of oxygen atoms in any sample of carbon dioxide.

Each molecule of carbon dioxide has 1 carbon atom and 2 oxygen atoms or a total of 3 atoms per molecule.

One out of 3 ($\frac{1}{3}$) atoms, or 33% of the atoms, are carbon atoms. ($\frac{1}{3} \times 100\% = 33\%$)

Two out of 3 ($\frac{2}{3}$) atoms, or 66% of the atoms, are oxygen atoms. ($\frac{2}{3} \times 100\% = 66\%$)

The table below shows you the chemical formulas for two common substances. Use the information to answer the questions below.

Chemical Formula for Two Common Substances

Compound	Elements in This Compound	Chemical Formula
ascorbic acid (vitamin C)	carbon, hydrogen, and oxygen	$C_6H_8O_6$
caffeine	carbon, hydrogen, nitrogen, and oxygen	$C_8H_{10}N_4O_2$

Find the percentage of each type of atom in a sample of ascorbic acid.

1. carbon: _____ $\frac{6}{20} = 30\%$

2. hydrogen: _____ $\frac{8}{20} = 40\%$

3. oxygen: _____ $\frac{6}{20} = 30\%$

Solve and Graph a Linear Equation

Bats use sound to navigate and hunt. As a bat flies, it sends out sound waves. These waves bounce off objects and return to the bat. Sound travels through warm air at about 343 meters per second. You can use the formula *speed (s) × time (t) = distance (d)* to calculate how long it takes a bat's sound to reach an object.

Example: To find out how long it takes for a bat's sound to reach a tree that is 10 meters away from the bat, substitute 10 m for *d* (distance) and 343 mps for *s* (speed). Solve for *t* (time). (Round to the nearest hundredth.)

$$343 \text{ mps} \times t = 10 \text{ m}$$

$$t = \frac{10}{343}$$

$$t = 0.029 \text{ or about 3 hundredths of a second}$$

Calculate how long it takes a bat's sound to bounce off the following objects.

1. a building at a distance of 5 meters _____0.015 seconds_____

2. a building at a distance of 20 meters _____0.06 seconds_____

3. a bridge at a distance of 30 meters _____0.09 seconds_____

4. Plot your results on a line graph. Let the *y*-axis show the time in seconds. Let the *x*-axis show the distance in meters.

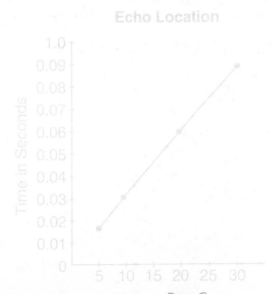

Echo Location

Scientific Notation

Scientists use scientific notation to write very large and very small numbers. A number in scientific notation is written in two parts. The first part is a number between 1 and 10. That number is multiplied by a power of ten.

Example: Light travels in a vacuum at a speed of about 300,000 km/s (kilometers per second).

> To write the number 300,000 in scientific notation, first place a decimal point in the number so that you have a number between 1 and 10. To find the power of ten, count the number of places you moved the decimal point.

$$300{,}000. = 3 \times 10^5$$

Solve.

1. The Sun is 150,000,000 (150 million) kilometers from Earth. Write this distance in scientific notation.

   $1.5 \times 10{,}000{,}000 = 1.5 \times 10^8$

2. In water, light travels about 225,000 km/sec. Write this speed in scientific notation.

   $2.25 \times 10{,}000 = 2.25 \times 10^5$

3. Light travels through a diamond at 124,000 km/sec. Write this speed in scientific notation.

   $1.24 \times 10{,}000 = 1.24 \times 10^5$

4. The mean distance between the Sun and Pluto is about 592,000,000,000 km. Write this distance in scientific notation.

   $5.92 \times 10{,}000{,}000{,}000 = 1.5 \times 10^{11}$

Use with page F54

Name _____ Date _____

Calculate Ratios

Power plants generate 155,000 to 765,000 volts of electrical current. When this high-voltage current reaches neighborhood power poles, transformers reduce the voltage to about 7,000 volts. Additional transformers reduce the current to 240 volts or 120 volts as it enters your home.

1. Suppose a power station generates an electrical current of 750,000 volts. A transformer on a power pole reduces that current to 7,500 volts. What is the ratio of the voltage at the power station to the voltage at the power pole?

   750,000 to 7,500 = 750,000:7,500 or 100 to 1
   _____

2. The voltage at the power pole is 7,500 volts. A transformer reduces the current to 120 volts to deliver into homes. What is the ratio of the voltage at the power pole to the voltage in the home current?

   $7{,}500 \text{ to } 120 = \frac{7{,}500}{120} = \frac{62.5}{1}$
   _____

3. A transformer in the black box at the end of a wireless telephone's power cord reduces the voltage from 120 volts to 9 volts. What is the ratio of the voltage at the wall outlet to the voltage used in a wireless telephone charger?

   $\frac{120}{9} = \frac{13.3}{1}$
   _____

4. When you plug your computer in a wall outlet, a transformer inside the computer reduces the voltage to 3 volts. What is the ratio of the voltage at the wall outlet to the voltage your computer uses?

   $\frac{120}{3} = \frac{40}{1}$
   _____

Make a Line Graph

The table shows a walker's data as she does a fitness course. The column on the left shows the cumulative time in 3-minute segments. The column on the right shows the walker's average speed for each 3-minute segment.

Use the data to make a line graph. Plot the time on the *x*-axis and the speed on the *y*-axis.

Cumulative time	Clocked speed	
0 min	0 km/hr	
3 min	5 km/hr	
6 min	5 km/hr	
9 min	5 km/hr	
12 min	0 km/hr	
15 min	0 km/hr	
18 min	6 km/hr	
21 min	6 km/hr	
24 min	2 km/hr	finish line
27 min	0 km/hr	

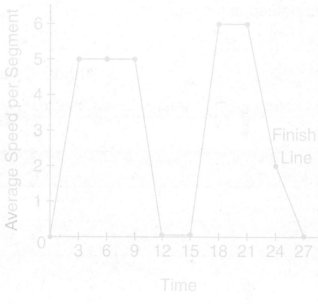

Narrative Writing: Animal Characteristics

Narrative writing tells a story about something that really happened in the writer's life.

Tell about an event with a pet or other animal.

Before you begin writing, make a list of the characteristics of the animal you have chosen.

Now, tell a story that involves some of the characteristics of animals explained in the chapter.

Animal Characteristics

All animals share certain characteristics.

_____

_____

_____

_____

_____

_____

_____

_____

_____

Answers will vary, but the narrative should include some of the

characteristics of animals that are mentioned in the chapter, such as

taking in food, having symmetry, needing oxygen, able to move.

Use with page A37

Explanatory Writing: Energy for Life

Explanatory writing tells how to make something or do something.

Plants both produce energy and use energy.

Before you begin writing, review what you've learned about photosynthesis and cell respiration.

Now, explain how plants produce or use energy.

Energy for Life

All living things need energy to survive.

_____

_____

_____

_____

_____

_____

_____

_____

Paragraphs will vary, but students should explain that through the process of photosynthesis, plants capture the Sun's energy and store it in the form of glucose. Plants and animals then use the stored energy for life processes by breaking down the glucose and releasing the energy—a process called respiration.

Use with page A49

Expository Writing: Eye Color

Expository writing presents, describes, and explains facts, ideas, and concepts.

Do you know where your traits come from?

Before you begin writing, list the eye color for all your family members.

Now, write a paragraph that outlines where your eye color comes from by tracing the trait to your parents and grandparents.

Eye Color

My eye color is _____.

Answers will vary. Students who do not have direct information about parents or grandparents should approach the assignment from the standpoint of what their parents must have had in order for them to have the traits that they do.

Explanatory Writing: Fossils

Explanatory writing tells how to make something or do something.

Fossils provide clues to organisms from the past.

Before you begin writing, review the different types of fossils.

Now, explain the ways that fossils can form.

Fossils

It can take thousands of years for a fossil to form.

_____

_____

_____

_____

_____

_____

_____

_____

_____

Answers will vary but students should describe the fact that over a long
period of time an organism can become buried in sediment and that
sediment will eventually become rock, leaving the imprint of the organism
in the rock. Student paragraphs should also include information on molds,
casts, imprints, and amber.

Use with page A118

Story Writing: A Plant's Life

Story writing tells a fictional tale with a beginning, a middle, and an end. A story has a plot, characters, and settings.

Think about how plants affect your daily life.

Before you begin writing, review the trophic levels of the basic food chain. How important are plants in the food chain?

Now, write a story from the point of view of a plant.

A Plant's Life

I am a plant, and I do not feel appreciated. _____

_____

_____

_____

_____

_____

_____

_____

_____

Answers will vary but students should discuss how plants are vital to food

webs and provide moisture and oxygen to the atmosphere. Writing should

be creative but detailed about the role of plants in the ecosystem.

Use with page B24

Expository Writing: Energy Flow

Expository writing presents, describes, and explains facts, ideas, and concepts.

Think about how energy moves through a food web. Where does energy begin? Where does it end?

Before you begin writing, think about your own place in the food chain.

Now, explain the flow of energy from the Sun to you. Choose specific examples of two different foods you've eaten this week.

Energy Flow

All energy begins with the Sun.

Answers will vary, but should include a detailed description of a food chain for each of the three foods named. One example: The Sun's energy is converted by grass. A cow eats the grass. Then, the cow becomes the hamburger I had for lunch. Some of the Sun's energy flows from the grass to the cow to me.

Use with page B50

Persuasive Writing: Biodiversity

Persuasive writing tries to persuade readers to agree with the writer or support the writer's ideas.

Biodiversity affects how well an ecosystem can survive change and disease.

Before you begin writing, review the history of the Irish Potato Famine.

Now, write a paragraph persuading local farmers to promote biodiversity by growing a variety of plants.

Biodiversity

Biodiversity will protect both your plants and your farms.

Paragraphs should explain that biodiversity means planting a variety of plants. Since most plant diseases affect only one species of plant, not all plants will be killed. Students should be persuasive in convincing farmers of biodiversity and perhaps use the Irish Potato Famine as an example.

Expository Writing: The Rock Cycle

Expository writing presents, describes, and explains facts, ideas, and concepts.

Despite their reputation, rocks move and change all the time.

Before you begin writing, review the rock cycle.

Now, describe the rock cycle for a sedimentary rock.

The Rock Cycle

The rock cycle begins with weathering.

_____

_____

_____

_____

_____

_____

_____

_____

_____

Paragraphs should explain that all types of surface rock are weathered

and eroded into sediment. The sediment is deposited elsewhere. Then

the sediment is compacted and cemented over a long period of time and

becomes new sedimentary rock. Then the cycle begins again.

Use with page C22

Expository Writing: Fossil Record

Expository writing presents, explains, and describes facts, ideas, and concepts.

Fossils provide important clues about Earth's history. These clues are part of the fossil record.

Before you begin writing, think about how fossils form and where they are found.

Now, describe at least three things about the past that scientists could learn from fossils. What is one of the procedures that they use?

Fossil Record

Fossils provide clues about several different parts of the past.

_____

_____

_____

_____

_____

_____

_____

Answers will vary, but should include at least three things that can be

learned by studying fossils (past climate, relative age of fossil, changes in

positions of the continents, reasons for extinctions) and one method used

by scientists to study fossils (relative dating).

Use with page C36

Persuasive Writing: Renewable Energy?

Persuasive writing tries to persuade readers to agree with the writer or support the writer's ideas.

People don't yet use renewable energy as much as they use nonrenewable energy.

Before you begin, think about the different types of renewable energy.

Now, persuade your reader to use more renewable sources of energy.

Renewable Energy?

Alternative, renewable sources of energy should be used whenever possible.

_____

_____

_____

_____

_____

_____

_____

_____

_____

Paragraphs should list all forms of renewable energy: solar, wind,

hydroelectric, nuclear, geothermal, and biomass. Students should explain

that these sources can help reduce the use of fossil fuels that are

nonrenewable and damaging to the environment.

Use with page C80

Narrative Writing: Weather and Me

Narrative writing tells a story about something that really happened in the writer's life.

Weather affects people's lives everyday.

Before you begin writing, think of some times when weather changed your plans. Were you caught in a storm? Was school cancelled after a big snowfall.

Now, tell about one of those times. Add an explanation of the type of weather that affected you.

Weather and Me

One day, the weather really changed my life.

_____

_____

_____

_____

_____

_____

_____

Answers will vary but students may recount a thunderstorm, a tornado,

a time when their flight was delayed by a snow storm, or countless other

possibilities. Make sure students provide some explanation for the event

based on their reading of the chapter.

Expository Writing: Tides

Expository writing presents, describes, and explains facts, ideas, and concepts.

People who live near the coast have to be aware of the tides.

Before you begin writing, think about how the tides could affect the lives of people on the coast.

Now, write a paragraph explaining what causes the tides to rise and fall.

Tides

The ocean's changing tides are caused by _____

_____

_____

_____

_____

_____

_____

_____

_____

Students should correctly explain what causes tides. Tides are caused by

primarily the pull of the Moon's gravity on Earth's oceans. The pull causes

the oceans to bulge out at the sides of the Earth facing toward and away

from the Moon. As Earth rotates, different points on Earth's surface are

located under tidal bulges.

Use with page D64

Story Writing: Another Planet

Story writing tells a fictional tale with a beginning, a middle, and an end. A story has a plot, characters, and settings.

Imagine what it would be like to live on another planet.

Before you begin writing, review what you know about the inner and outer planets.

Now, write a story about what it would be like to live on another planet. Choose a planet and use its characteristics in your story.

Another Planet

Life is exciting here! _____

_____

_____

_____

_____

_____

_____

_____

_____

Stories will vary, but should include facts from the textbook about the

chosen planet, as well as imaginative details about how everyday life

would be different on that planet.

Name _____ Date _____

Story Writing: Inside an Atom

Story writing tells a fictional tale with a beginning, a middle, and an end. A story has a plot, characters, and settings.

What would happen if you were small enough to crawl inside an atom?

Before you begin writing, list the parts of the atom.

Now, write a story about a student who shrinks and is able to explore an atom.

Inside an Atom

When I woke up, I could tell that I had shrunk to the size of the tiniest speck. I looked over and saw

Answers will vary, but the story should include an accurate description of the structure of an atom, as well as correctly use the terms nucleus, protons, neutrons, and electrons.

Use with page E6

Story Writing: Chemical Change

Story writing tells a fictional tale with a beginning, a middle, and an end. A story has a plot, characters, and settings.

Chemical changes happen everyday.

Before you begin writing, list as many chemical changes as you can think of that you might see in a typical day.

Now, write a story about how a chemical change could affect your day.

Chemical Change

My day began as usual. _____

_____

_____

_____

_____

_____

_____

_____

_____

_____

Stories will vary, but should explain at least one chemical change. Stories should be detailed and creative.

Use with page E50

Explanatory Writing: Hot Pot!

Explanatory writing tells how to make something or do something.

You've probably seen a pot of water being heated.

Before you begin writing, discuss the transfer of thermal energy with your class.

Now, explain how a pot of water heats up.

Hot Pot!

Water heats up because _____

_____

_____

_____

_____

_____

_____

_____

_____

_____

_____

Students should explain that water heats up when thermal energy is

transferred by conduction from the stove via the pot to the water. The

heated water expands and rises because its density decreases. Cooler

water from the top of the pan sinks to the bottom, where it is heated. A

convection current is set up.

Use with page F26

Name _____ Date _____

Persuasive Writing: Sunlight Safety

Persuasive writing tries to persuade readers to agree with the writer or support the writer's ideas.

Many people work or play in the sunlight all day long.

Before you begin writing, think about the dangers of ultraviolet rays and light.

Now, persuade your readers to practice sunlight safety.

Sunlight Safety

Even though sunlight feels good, it can be harmful to our bodies.

_____

_____

_____

_____

_____

_____

_____

_____

Answers will vary, but should include facts from the textbook about

the dangerous effects of too much exposure to sunlight, for example

the danger of sunburns, skin cancer, and the possibility of early skin

aging. Sunlight can also damage eyes—sunglasses can help protect your

eyes from sunlight.

Explanatory Writing: Electricity

Explanatory writing tells how to make something or do something.

Electricity powers many things in your home.

Before you begin writing, list all the electrical appliances in your home.

Now, choose an electrical appliance and explain how electricty travels from the power plant to your home to the appliance.

Electricity

Electricity provides power to _____

_____

_____

_____

_____

_____

_____

_____

_____

Answers will vary, but should include a description of electricity traveling

through power lines and transformers to get from the power plant to

homes, then through circuits in the home. Students should describe

how an object is plugged into a circuit through wall outlets, or how wall

switches open and close circuits.

Narrative Writing: Simple Machines

Narrative writing tells a story about something that really happened in the writer's life.

Simple machines can help make a variety of work easier.

Before you begin writing, review each type of simple machine.

Now, write about a time that a simple machine made work easier for you.

Simple Machines

A simple machine helped me when _____

_____

_____

_____

_____

_____

_____

_____

_____

_____

_____

_____

Narratives should tell a detailed story about a simple machine helping the student do some kind of work. Students could choose levers, wheel and axle, pulleys, inclined planes, wedges, or screws.

Chapter 1

Vocabulary

Complete each sentence with a term from the list.

1. ___Invertebrates___ are animals without a backbone.

2. ___Angiosperms___ are vascular plants that produce flowers.

3. Frogs and salamanders are examples of ___amphibians___.

4. Some ___bacteria___ have lived on Earth longer than any other organism.

5. In ___vascular___ plants, tube-like tissues transport water through the plant.

6. A tool that helps you to identify an organism by asking a series of questions is called a(n) ___dichotomous key___.

7. Whether safe to eat or not, all mushrooms are ___fungi___.

8. Different ___protists___ have characteristics of fungi, plants, and animals.

9. Jellyfish with stinging tentacles are classified as ___cnidarians___.

10. ___Nonvascular___ plants absorb water in a similar way to a sponge soaking up a liquid.

amphibians A33

angiosperms A20

bacteria A8

cnidarians A30

dichotomous key A7

fungi A12

gymnosperm A18

invertebrates A30

kingdom A6

nonvascular A17

protist A10

protozoa A10

symmetry A30

vascular A17

Use with pages A40–A41

Test Prep

Write the letter of the best answer choice.

11. Conifers are _____C_____ that
have male and female cones that
are used for reproduction.

   A angiosperms

   B cycads

   C gymnosperms

   D algae

12. One unique characteristic of animals
is that they _____B_____.

   A have only one cell

   B eat food

   C can create energy from the Sun

   D cannot move from place to place

13. _____D_____ are animal-like
protists.

   A Algae

   B Mammals

   C Mosses

   D Protozoa

14. _____A_____ are vascular plants
that reproduce through cones.

   A Gymnosperms

   B Club mosses

   C Angiosperms

   D Ferns

Inquiry Skills

15. Compare Look at the photos in your book of the maple tree and
meerkats. Identify which kingdom each organism comes from.
Compare and contrast the characteristics of the two kingdoms.

maple tree: plant kingdom (plantae); meerkat: animal kingdom

(animalia). Both are multicellular organisms; both need water

and nutrients. Plants use energy from the Sun and carbon

dioxide to make food, and give off more oxygen than carbon

dioxide. Animals can move, get food from outside their

bodies, breathe in oxygen, and exhale carbon dioxide.

_____

_____

_____

16. **Classify** Name three types of organisms that display bilateral symmetry. Describe features of each organism that demonstrate this form of symmetry.

Students should choose three of the following groups: worms, mollusks, arthropods, and vertebrates. Descriptions should include features that have bilateral symmetry.

Critical Thinking

17. **Synthesize** How could new knowledge change the way we classify organisms?

DNA testing might show that organisms thought to be related are not.

18. **Evaluate** Explain how certain physical characteristics have helped fish live in water.

Fish have gills that extract oxygen from the water, and fins and streamlined bodies to help them swim.

19. **Apply** You have found what looks to be a new kind of plant. How would you determine if it is a plant?

Look at tissue samples through a microscope. Plants are multicellular and have tissues and organs; their cells would have cell walls and chloroplasts.

20. **Analyze** What are the characteristics of vascular plants?

Vascular plants have tube-like tissues that allow the plant to transport water and nutrients throughout the plant.

Chapter 2

Vocabulary
Complete each sentence with a term from the list.

1. The ____chloroplast____ is the organelle where photosynthesis occurs.

2. Cells of the ____immune system____ produce antibodies.

3. Molecules move from an area of higher concentration to one of lower concentration during ____diffusion____.

4. The ____nucleus____ is the control center of a cell.

5. ____Hormones____ are released by the endocrine system.

6. The gel-like material that surrounds all parts of the cell inside the cell membrane is the ____cytoplasm____.

7. The ____musculoskeletal system____ provides support for the human body and enables body movement.

8. Cholera and salmonella poisoning are examples of a(n) ____infectious disease____.

9. ____Organs____ are made of two or more types of tissue that perform particular functions.

10. The arteries are part of the ____circulatory system____.

chloroplast A47
circulatory system A56
cytoplasm A47
diffusion A48
hormones A58
immune system A69
infectious disease A66
musculoskeletal system A57
nervous system A56
non-infectious disease A67
nucleus A47
organelle A47
organs A55
osmosis A48
tissue A54

Test Prep

Write the letter of the best answer choice.

11. Blood moves throughout the body in
_____C_____.

  A passive transport

  B organelles

  C the circulatory system

  D epithelial tissue

12. Special blood proteins that fight disease are _____C_____.

  A inflammation

  B phagocytes

  C antibodies

  D immunities

13. Active transport requires
_____C_____.

  A the nervous system

  B osmosis

  C the input of energy

  D the muscular system

14. Glucose and oxygen combine to release energy in a process called _____C_____.

  A photosynthesis

  B mitosis

  C respiration

  D inflammation

Inquiry Skills

15. Use Models Identify and describe the process modeled in the illustration in your book.

The immune response is illustrated. Cells recognize an invading virus; the cells attack and destroy infected body cells. Antibodies remain in the blood, so if the same virus invades again, the immune response will be faster.

16. Infer A particular organ in the human body releases a substance that causes other cells in the body to divide and grow. What body system does this organ belong to?

The organ belongs to the endocrine system.

Use with pages A74–A75

Critical Thinking

17. Analyze Could an organism survive only by using passive transport, never active transport? Explain.

No, some materials need to move into areas of higher

concentration.

_____

_____

18. Inferring The results of a blood test show much higher levels of white blood cells than is normal. What might this indicate?

It might mean the person has a disease.

_____

_____

_____

19. Synthesize Give some examples of organs from different systems in the body that work together. Discuss what they accomplish.

Sample answer: The brain controls many muscle movements.

_____

_____

_____

20. Apply Ten horses sleep in the same barn. After one week, one of the horses becomes sick, but the others do not. What kind of disease does the sick horse probably have?

Sample answer: The horse has a non-infectious disease.

_____

_____

_____

Use with pages A74–A75

Chapter 3

Vocabulary
Complete each sentence with a term from the list.

1. The process in which cells copy their DNA is called _____replication_____.

2. __Asexual reproduction__ occurs when an organism divides in half to produce offspring.

3. A _____hybrid_____ is the offspring of two parents from different purebred strains.

4. The alternate forms of a gene are called _____alleles_____.

5. Proteins are synthesized in _____ribosomes_____.

6. Before _____mitosis_____, the cell duplicates its chromosomes.

7. __Incomplete dominance__ occurs when a dominant allele for a trait is only partly expressed.

8. Gamete cells are produced during _____meiosis_____.

9. A change in a base pair is called a(n) _____mutation_____.

10. In some plants, pink flowers result from parents that carry _____codominant_____ alleles for color.

alleles A90

asexual reproduction A80

codominant A93

DNA A94

hybrid A91

incomplete dominance A93

meiosis A94

mitosis A82

mutation A106

replication A104

ribosomes A105

sexual reproduction A81

Name _____ Date _____

Test Prep

Write the letter of the best answer choice.

11. RNA is important in building
_____C_____.

   A alleles

   B gametes

   C proteins

   D chromosomes

12. Crick, Watson, Franklin, and Wilkins all contributed to discovering the structure of _____A_____.

   A DNA

   B mRNA

   C tRNA

   D proteins

13. A new organism is usually reproduced by the joining of _____A_____.

   A an egg and a sperm

   B two matching base pairs

   C the different sides of a double helix

   D two ribosomes

14. In sexual reproduction, offspring receive _____C_____.

   A only dominant alleles

   B only recessive alleles

   C genetic material from two parents

   D genetic material from only one parent

Inquiry Skills

15. Research *Caenorhabditis elegans* is a small worm that is very useful for studying genetics. Find out why this worm is so useful, or research other organisms that scientists study to learn about genetics. Write a paragraph to show your findings.

This tiny worm's genome has been completely sequenced.

The worm is easy to grow and manipulate in the lab.

16. Predict In humans, the allele for brown eyes (*B*) is dominant over the allele for blue eyes (*b*). Draw a PunnettSquare like the one below. Use it to predict the offspring from two brown-eyed parents who each carry the allele for blue eyes. One out of four offspring is likely to have blue eyes.

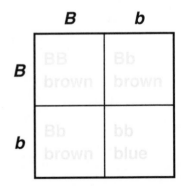

Use with pages A112–A113

Critical Thinking

17. Analyze What are some similarities and differences between asexual reproduction and sexual reproduction?

In asexual reproduction, a single parent divides to produce offspring, and characteristics are directly inherited (no variation). In sexual reproduction, two parents produce offspring that inherit traits from each; this type of reproduction leads to more variation.

18. Compare How is DNA organized similarly to a set of encyclopedias?

DNA contains a huge amount of information organized into different "volumes," or chromosomes. The information is also organized into genes, which are like the individual articles of an encyclopedia.

19. Synthesize Explain the relationship between beneficial mutations in food crops or farm animals, and the practice of selective breeding.

Sample answer: A farmer may notice that some strawberry plants are producing tastier fruit, a change that occurred due to a good mutation. The farmer can then breed these plants to produce offspring that consistently produce tastier fruit.

20. Evaluate How will an understanding of DNA and the human genome benefit science?

A better understanding of the human genome will help scientists understand how our bodies work and how illnesses occur. This understanding could lead to new treatments.

Student Resources

251

Use with pages A112–A113

Chapter 4

Vocabulary
Complete each sentence with a term from the list. You may use each term more than once.

1. An insect preserved in amber is an example of a(n) _____fossil_____.

2. When humans breed dogs, they are using the process of _selective breeding_.

3. ____Extinction____ is the disappearance of all members of a species.

4. Scientists believe that the presence of _homologous structures_ in different animals is strong evidence of a common ancestor.

5. _Natural selection_ occurs when individuals that are better adapted to their environment survive, while those that are less well adapted do not.

6. The _geologic time scale_ consists of four eras: the Precambrian, the Paleozoic, the Mesozoic, and the Cenozoic.

7. The _____fossil_____ record provides important scientific evidence about ancient organisms and their environment.

8. At the end of the Mesozoic era, many organisms, including the dinosaurs, died out in a(n) _mass extinction_.

9. As giraffes evolved, the ones with the longest necks had a better chance of survival. This is an example of _natural selection_.

10. The ____extinction____ of one species can allow another species to thrive.

extinction A120
fossil A118
geologic time scale A120
homologous structures A132
mass extinction A120
natural selection A129
selective breeding A128

Test Prep

Write the letter of the best answer choice.

11. The geologic time scale is divided into _____B_____.

  A eras, extinctions, and mass extinctions

  B eons, eras, and periods

  C eons, periods, and epochs

  D eons, eras, and extinctions

12. Which of these organisms was NOT studied by Charles Darwin during his trip to the Galapagos Islands? _____A_____

  A bats

  B finches

  C tortoises

  D iguanas

13. The geologic time scale is based on _____D_____.

  A the theory of natural selection

  B plate tectonics

  C the extinction of dinosaurs

  D fossil evidence

14. Charles Darwin based his ideas about change over time on the theory of _____C_____.

  A selective breeding

  B natural breeding

  C natural selection

  D geologic time scale

Inquiry Skills

15. Compare Compare the bone structure of the limbs in the animals shown in the illustration in your book.

The cat's foreleg and the bat's wing both contain the same bones. In each animal, the bones are adapted for different uses.

16. Infer Monarch butterflies are poisonous to their predators. Why would it be beneficial for other butterflies to look like a monarch? How might this be related to natural selection?

Being poisonous to predators is an adaptive trait. Butterflies that mimic this trait are more likely to be avoided by predators, and therefore more likely to survive and have offspring.

Critical Thinking

17. Apply Suppose that a cut on your finger becomes infected by some bacteria. Explain how and why some bacteria might survive in your cut even if you treat it with antibiotics.

Resistant bacteria survive the antibiotics, while nonresistant bacteria are killed. So the resistant bacteria grow and multiply, reducing the chances that the antibiotics will destroy the bacteria.

18. Analyze Why is the extinction of some organisms important to the development of other organisms? Explain your answer.

The extinction of some organisms allows other organisms to thrive.

19. Evaluate How did Darwin's ideas influence the science of biology?

Darwin showed that variation among organisms was the result of inherited traits. He also showed that individuals with traits that adapted well to the environment had a greater chance of survival and reproduction. His theory was the best explanation of the known facts. It has since been supported by much scientific evidence.

20. Synthesize How could homologous structure evolve in different species that live in different parts of the world?

Many traits evolve over time as adaptations to some environmental circumstance. Although the ancestors of these organisms evolved in different areas of the world, the environments in which they evolved may have been similar.

Chapter 5

Vocabulary

Complete each sentence with a term from the list.

1. During the process of ___photosynthesis___, plants make glucose and release oxygen into the air.

2. Plants and animals use oxygen to release the energy in food during the process of ___respiration___.

3. The process certain bacteria use to change a gas in the air to a compound that plants can use is ___nitrogen fixation___.

4. Water changes from a liquid to a gas during ___evaporation___ and ___transpiration___.

5. An organism that can make its own food is a(n) ___producer___.

6. An organism that eats other organisms for food is a(n) ___consumer___.

7. A(n) ___decomposer___ breaks down dead organisms and returns chemicals to soil.

8. Rain and snow are forms of ___precipitation___.

9. A(n) ___energy pyramid___ is a model that shows how much energy moves from one trophic level to another.

10. A(n) ___food web___ illustrates the complex relationships in an ecological community.

consumer B24

decomposer B26

energy pyramid B27

evaporation B16

food web B25

nitrogen fixation B14

photosynthesis B6

precipitation B16

producer B24

respiration B7

transpiration B16

trophic level B24

Test Prep

Write the letter of the best answer choice.

11. Which gases cycle in opposite directions between plants and animals? _____A_____

  A oxygen and carbon dioxide

  B oxygen and water

  C nitrogen and carbon dioxide

  D nitrogen and water

12. What takes up carbon dioxide from the atmosphere? _____A_____

  A a tree growing

  B fossil fuels burning

  C animals breathing

  D a forest burning

13. What nutrient can animals get only by eating plants or other animals? _____B_____

  A oxygen

  B nitrogen

  C carbon dioxide

  D water

14. About how much energy is passed from one level in an energy pyramid to the next level? _____A_____

  A 10%

  B 50%

  C 90%

  D 100%

Inquiry Skills

15. Predict What might happen to the other trophic levels in a food web if the number of primary consumers decreased drastically?

The number of secondary and tertiary consumers would

decrease because they would have lost their source of food.

16. Infer A field has had corn harvested from it for five years in a row. Each year the field produces less corn. Why might the plants be producing less corn? Explain your answer.

The corn plants are not getting enough nitrogen. The corn

plants in the previous years used nitrogen compounds from

the soil. When the corn was harvested, the nitrogen in the

plants was removed from the field instead of being returned

to the soil by decomposers.

Critical Thinking

17. Apply Imagine you are stranded on an island with limited space and have to grow your own food. You have seeds for growing corn and wheat. You also have a few pigs and cows. What will you choose to grow for food? Explain your answer.

Sample answer: I will grow corn and wheat. The amount of

energy available from eating animals is only about 10% of

the energy that is available by eating the plants.

_____

18. Synthesize If you had the ability to carry out photosynthesis, how would your life be different?

Sample answer: I wouldn't have to eat, so I wouldn't have to

buy food. I would have to spend much of my day in sunlight.

_____

19. Analyze What is the relationship between decomposers and other organisms?

Decomposers break down the wastes of other organisms

and the organisms themselves when they die. They return

chemicals to the soil to be used by other organisms.

_____

20. Evaluate What would you say to someone who told you that there is plenty of water, so it does not matter how much we use or if we pollute it?

Only about 1% of the water on Earth is usable. In addition,

pollutants can contaminate water, making it unusable.

_____

_____

Use with pages B32–B33

Chapter 6

Vocabulary

Complete each sentence with a term from the list.

1. All the different species living in one place, along with their nonliving environment, make up a(n) _____ecosystem_____.

2. _____Biotic factors_____ are the living parts of an ecosystem.

3. The nonliving parts of an ecosystem are its _____abiotic factors_____.

4. _____Omnivores_____ eat both plants and animals.

5. A land area with similar climate conditions and living things throughout is a(n) _____biome_____.

6. _____Carnivores_____ hunt and eat other animals.

7. _____Commensalism_____ is a relationship in which one species benefits while the other species is neither harmed nor helped.

8. Animals that eat only plants are called _____herbivores_____.

9. The unique role of each species in an ecosystem is called its ecological _____niche_____.

10. An animal that is eaten by a predator is called _____prey_____.

abiotic factors B38
biome B40
biotic factors B38
carnivores B50
commensalism B59
ecosystem B38
herbivores B50
mutualism B59
niche B48
omnivores B50
parasitism B60
prey B48
symbiosis B58

Use with pages B66–B67

Test Prep

Write the letter of the best answer choice.

11. If a rabbit is a fox's prey, then the fox is the rabbit's _____C_____.

A omnivore

B producer

C predator

D parasite

12. The part of the ocean ecosystem in which you would expect to find a barnacle is the _____A_____.

A intertidal zone

B neritic zone

C upper open ocean

D deep open ocean

13. A biome that has permafrost and no trees is the _____D_____.

A grassland

B taiga

C desert

D tundra

14. Tapeworms and ticks are common examples of _____B_____.

A hosts

B parasites

C commensalism

D predators

Inquiry Skills

15. Use Numbers The average July temperature in an ecosystem in 20°C. The average temperature in February is −8°C. The average rainfall in June is 50 mm. The average rainfall in February is 10 mm. What can you infer about the ecosystem's climate?

The ecosystem has a cold season and a warm season. It

gets moderate rainfall, with more in summer than in winter.

16. Use Models You design and color paper to look like different insects. After placing the insects around the classroom, you give your classmates 30 seconds to find all the insects they can. What are some reasons why some insects were found and others were not found? If these were real insects, how would their appearance affect their relationships with other species?

Some insects were harder to see than others. Insects that

can be seen more easily are more likely to become prey.

Critical Thinking

17. Apply Would a tree that normally grows in a temperate forest be able to survive in a desert? Explain your answer.

No, it would need more water than it could get in the

desert.

_____

18. Synthesize What would happen to an ecosystem if there were no decomposers?

Waste and dead organisms would never decay. The nutrients

in their bodies would be tied up forever, and the ecosystem

would fail.

_____

19. Evaluate Tests performed by scientists show that eagles living near a particular river have ten times the DDT levels of the fish they catch. Does this data support the idea of biomagnification? Explain your answer.

Yes, biomagnification says that the level of certain

substances, such as pesticides, in an ecosystem are

magnified the further up the food chain they are found. The

eagle is at the top of a food chain.

_____

20. Analyze What is the difference between a parasite and a predator?

A parasite lives on or in its host, and its survival depends

on the host's survival. A predator kills its prey.

_____

Use with pages B66–B67

Chapter 7

Vocabulary

Complete each sentence with a term from the list.

1. _Primary succession_ occurs after new land is created or exposed.

2. The variety of natural plants and animals that live in an ecosystem is called _biodiversity_.

3. The first organisms to move into newly disturbed or exposed land are _pioneer species_.

4. _Invasive species_ are plants or animals imported to an ecosystem that often have no natural predators.

5. A mature ecosystem remaining mostly stable over time is a(n) _climax community_.

6. Competition, predation, and disease are all _limiting factors_ affecting population growth.

7. _Competition_ is the use of the same resources by organisms with similar needs.

8. Animals catching prey practice _predation_.

9. The consequence of an unbalanced ecosystem can be the disappearance of a species, or _extinction_.

10. Changes in an ecosystem over time in an area that already has soil are part of _secondary succession_.

biodiversity B82

competition B73

climax community B85

disease B75

extinction B76

invasive species B75

limiting factors B72

pioneer species B84

predation B74

primary succession B84

secondary succession B85

Test Prep

Write the letter of the best answer choice.

11. One reason for population explosions among invasive species is that they _____B_____.

  A have no prey

  B have no predators

  C compete poorly for resources

  D cause diseases

12. Which causes extinction? _____D_____

  A habitat destruction

  B invasive species

  C overharvesting

  D all of the above

13. Which is true about ecological succession? _____A_____

  A It slows as an ecosystem matures.

  B It only occurs in disturbed areas.

  C Invasive species slow it down.

  D It decreases biodiversity.

14. Pioneer species _____D_____.

  A subtract from biodiversity

  B cannot survive in mature areas

  C are slow growing

  D need few nutrients and grow fast

Inquiry Skills

15. Use Numbers After a clean-up, the trout population in a particular river doubles every year for five years. If there were 100 trout to start with, how many are there after five years?

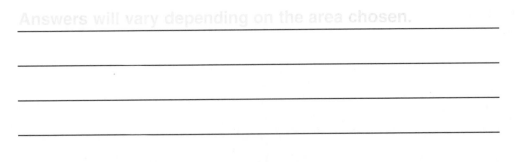

$100 \times 2 \times 2 \times 2 \times 2 \times 2 = 3,200$ trout

16. Collaborate With a partner, discuss an area near where you live that you would like to see set aside as a nature preserve. Write a paragraph describing the area and reasons for preserving it.

Answers will vary depending on the area chosen.

_____

_____

_____

_____

Critical Thinking

17. Apply Why are the native animals of islands especially vulnerable to invasive species?

Animals on islands, such as the moa of New Zealand and the

nene of Hawaii, typically have not adapted to a wide range of

other species living with them. When such species arrive on

the island, the ecosystem can change dramatically.

18. Synthesize How would you improve chances of keeping invasive species out of North America? Do you think this is an important goal? Explain.

Sample answer: Enact laws forbidding or regulating animal

andplant imports from other countries. Educate gardeners and

others in the general public about planting invasive plants.

Yes, I think this is an important goal because it protects native

species.

19. Evaluate Consider this statement: "Habitat destruction is necessary for the health of the U.S. economy." Do you agree or disagree? Explain your answer.

Answers should be supported with sound reasoning.

20. Analyze What is the relationship between biodiversity and ecosystem stability? Explain. Include an example in your answer.

Biodiversity measures the number of species in an ecosystem.

Ecosystem stability indicates that the community's species are

at their carrying capacity. Biodiversity encourages ecosystem

stability, because if one species is removed, another may take

its place. An example of the effects of a lack of biodiversity

was the Irish Potato Famine in the 1840s.

263

Use with pages B92–B93

Chapter 8

Vocabulary

Complete each sentence with a term from the list. You may use each term more than once.

1. Rocks continually change from one type to another in a series of processes called the _____rock cycle_____.

2. You can rub a mineral along a rough surface to observe its _____streak_____.

3. _____Igneous rock_____ is formed when magma cools and crystallizes.

4. Minerals that break apart along planes when struck have _____cleavage_____.

5. When clay, mud, and sand are deposited and buried over millions of years, _____sedimentary rock_____ is produced.

6. The way that the surface of a mineral reflects light is called its _____luster_____.

7. All samples of the same _____mineral_____ have the same chemical makeup.

8. Scratching an unknown mineral sample with different known minerals can help estimate its _____hardness_____.

9. Heat and pressure can deform sedimentary rock into _____metamorphic rock_____.

10. Weathering and erosion are part of the _____rock cycle_____.

cleavage C9

hardness C8

igneous rock C17

luster C9

metamorphic rock C17

mineral C6

rock cycle C22

sedimentary rock C17

streak C9

Use with pages C28–C29

Test Prep

Write the letter of the best answer choice.

11. A mineral's hardness is determined by its _____D_____.

   A color

   B streak

   C cleavage

   D crystal structure

12. Magma that cools slowly can produce _____B_____ crystals.

   A small

   B large

   C light

   D dark

13. Rocks are best described as _____A_____.

   A mixtures

   B elements

   C structures

   D compounds

14. High temperature and pressure can change limestone into _____C_____.

   A shells

   B granite

   C marble

   D quartzite

Inquiry Skills

15. Use Numbers Suppose you are studying part of a sedimentary rock formation that is 3 m thick. You have estimated that each centimeter of rock was laid down over a 300-year period. Fill in the chart below to give the estimated relative age of the rock at each distance from the top.

Age of Sedimentary Rock

Distance (m)	Age
0.5	50 years
1	100 years
1.5	150 years
2	200 years
2.5	250 years
3	300 years

Use with pages C28–C29

16. **Observe** Study the photo of the desert landscape on page C21. Describe the picture in your own words. What types of changes formed the structures you see?

The rocks are sedimentary rocks that likely formed at the

bottom of an ancient ocean. Over time, wind and water

eroded the rocks into their current shapes.

Critical Thinking

17. **Evaluate** What would you say to someone who said that landscapes and rock formations are permanent features?

Sample answer: I would explain the rock cycle. Also, I

would explain that erosion and weathering affect landscape

and rock formations, as do movements of Earth, such as

mountain formation, volcanic eruptions, and earthquakes.

18. **Apply** Which physical properties would you look for if you were choosing a mineral to use as a piece of jewelry?

Sample answer: Luster would be the most important

physical property. If it were jewelry that would be worn

daily, hardness would be important.

19. **Analyze** What can you infer about the formation of a piece of granite that contains mostly large white and pink crystals?

The granite likely was formed from melted rock material that

was white and pink. The material probably cooled over a

long period of time, resulting in large crystals.

20. **Synthesize** How would the rock cycle on Earth be different if Earth, like the Moon, did not have an atmosphere?

There would be no wind or rain to weather and erode rocks.

Chapter 9

Vocabulary

Complete each sentence with a term from the list.

1. Earth's lithosphere is broken up into
   ___tectonic plates___.

2. The preserved remains of a plant or an animal in
   the rock record is called a _____fossil_____.

3. Sedimentary rock is deposited in layers called
   _____strata_____.

4. A(n) _____tsunami_____ is a huge ocean wave
   usually caused by an earthquake.

5. Earthquakes produce ___seismic waves___ that can
   travel far from the focus.

6. The _____mantle_____ is a thick layer of dense
   rock below Earth's crust.

7. When magma flows up and fills the space at many
   divergent boundaries, ___sea-floor spreading___ occurs.

8. The _____lithosphere_____ is made of Earth's crust and the upper
   part of the mantle.

9. The place along a fault where rock first begins to move during
   an earthquake is called the _____focus_____.

10. The thin outer layer of Earth is called the _____crust_____.

crust C45

epicenter C54

focus C54

fossil C36

lithosphere C45

mantle C45

plate boundary C52

sea-floor spreading C46

seismic waves C54

strata C35

tectonic plates C45

tsunami C52

Use with pages C62–C63

Name _____ Date _____

Test Prep

Write the letter of the best answer choice.

11. The hypothesis of ___B___ states that the continents were once massed together in a supercontinent called Pangea.

- **A** plate tectonics
- **B** continental drift
- **C** sea-floor spreading
- **D** convergent boundaries

12. Geologic activities such as earthquakes and volcanoes often occur ___A___.

- **A** at plate boundaries
- **B** in the core
- **C** under sedimentary layers
- **D** near the center of continents

13. The ___C___ of an earthquake is the spot on Earth's surface directly over the place where the rock began to move along the fault.

- **A** focus
- **B** scale
- **C** epicenter
- **D** magnitude

14. Because tectonic plates are constantly being created and destroyed, the ___C___ on Earth are relatively young.

- **A** continents
- **B** volcanoes
- **C** ocean floors
- **D** mountain chains

Inquiry Skills

15. Infer A region has just experienced a series of major earthquakes. What can you infer about that region's position on its underlying tectonic plates?

The region is likely on a plate boundary.

16. Use Models How would you design a model that shows different types of plate boundaries?

Accept any accurate model design. Sample answer:

Two foam blocks representing plates can be used to

demonstrate movement of the plates

Name _____ Date _____

Critical Thinking

17. Infer What could you conclude about an area where new sea floor was forming from cooling magma?

The area contains a divergent plate boundary along a mid-ocean ridge.

18. Evaluate Consider the fossil evidence that Wegener used to support his hypothesis of continental drift. What facts related to the fossils did he use? What conclusions did he draw from those facts?

Wegener noted that fossils of freshwater animals from South America were very similar to those found in Western Africa. From this, Wegener concluded that the two continents must have been connected at some time in the past.

19. Apply Los Angeles is located on the Pacific Plate, which is moving northwest at a rate of 46 mm (2 in.) per year. How far from its present location will Los Angeles have moved in 1,000 years?

In 1,000 years, Los Angeles will have moved 46 m (50 yd) from its present location.

20. Analyze What is the difference between P-waves, S-waves, and surface waves?

P-waves travel fastest and are first to arrive at a given location. They have a push-pull motion and can travel through solids, liquids, and gases. S-waves come after P-waves. They cause the ground to shake from side to side and can only travel through solids. Surface waves travel in a rolling motion across Earth's surface.

Chapter 10

Vocabulary

Complete each sentence with a term from the list. You may use each term more than once.

1. Plant parts, sawdust, bark, and food waste are all examples of _____biomass_____.

2. Since fossil fuels take millions of years to replace, they are called ___nonrenewable resources___.

3. Hot springs and geysers are examples of ____geothermal energy____.

4. Photovoltaic cells use ____solar energy____ to make electricity.

5. ___Renewable resources___ can be used day after day without running out.

6. Energy from the Sun is called ____solar energy____.

7. Coal, petroleum oil, and natural gas are all ____fossil fuels____.

8. When moving water is used to make electricity, it is called ___hydroelectric energy___.

9. Cars that run on ethanol or biodiesel are using the energy stored in ____biomass____.

10. The Sun, wind, and moving water are all examples of ___renewable resources___.

biomass C86

fossil fuels C68

geothermal energy C85

hydroelectric energy C83

nonrenewable resources C71

renewable resources C80

solar energy C81

Name _____ Date _____

Test Prep

Write the letter of the best answer choice.

11. Nuclear power plants use
_____D_____ to produce energy.

  A biomass

  B coal

  C wind

  D uranium

12. _____A_____ were made from
the remains of plants that lived in
swamps some 300 million years ago.

  A Fossil fuels

  B Nuclear fuels

  C Biomass

  D Hydrogen cells

13. Geothermal power plants use hot
_____D_____ from deep in the
ground to make electricity.

  A gas

  B soil

  C coal

  D water

14. In a hydrogen fuel cell, hydrogen
reacts with _____C_____ to
produce energy and water.

  A water

  B wind

  C oxygen

  D carbon dioxide

Inquiry Skills

15. Use Numbers Imagine a day in the future when the world's oil
reserves are 3 trillion barrels. Demand at that time is 50 billion
barrels per year. At that rate of use, how much longer would the
reserves last?

3 trillion/50 billion = 60 years

16. Use Models Using the illustration in your book as a model,
explain how solar energy can be used to heat a house.

Answers will vary, but should explain how solar energy is

used.

_____

_____

_____

Critical Thinking

17. Apply What are some ways that you can practice energy conservation in your daily life?

Examples of energy conservation include turning off

electrical devices when not in use, recycling, wearing

appropriate clothing to reduce need for heating and air

conditioning, and insulating homes to reduce energy use.

18. Analyze What is the difference between the way solar energy is used in solar collectors and photovoltaic cells?

In solar water heaters, solar energy is used to heat water

directly; in photovoltaic cells, solar energy is used to

produce electricity to power devices.

19. Evaluate How did the information in Chapter 10 change the way you think about how you use energy in your daily life?

Answers will vary, but should relate information in the

chapter to students' personal energy consumption.

20. Synthesize How is energy from the Sun used in both renewable and nonrenewable energy resources?

The Sun is the original source of energy in renewable

resources such as solar, wind, hydroelectric, and biomass.

It is also the original source of energy in fossil fuels such

as coal, oil, and methane.

Chapter 11

Vocabulary
Complete each sentence with a term from the list.

1. A(n) _____hurricane_____ is a powerful storm that forms over warm ocean waters.

2. The loop created by warm air rising and cool air sinking is called a _____convection current_____ .

3. Westerlies and other winds that blow in a particular direction are called _____prevailing winds_____ .

4. The area where two air masses meet is called a(n) _____front_____ .

5. A severe storm with high winds and snow is called a(n) _____blizzard_____ .

6. _____Precipitation_____ is water, snow, or ice that falls from clouds.

7. The long-term weather patterns for an area are its _____climate_____ .

8. A strong storm that forms at a front where warm, moist air rises above cooler air is called a(n) _____thunderstorm_____

9. The _____jet stream_____ is a belt of winds in the upper troposphere.

10. The bending of global winds is due to the _____Coriolis effect_____ .

air mass D12
atmosphere D6
blizzard D33
climate D20
convection current D9
Coriolis effect D18
front D13
hurricane D34
jet stream D19
ocean current D20
precipitation D10
prevailing winds D19
thunderstorm D32
tornado D36

Use with pages D40–D41

Test Prep

Write the letter of the best answer choice.

11. Maritime polar and continental tropical are names for _____ D _____ .

A storms

B clouds

C fronts

D air masses

13. Which of these severe storms is especially common in the Great Plains, and less common elsewhere? _____ C _____

A thunderstorms

B blizzards

C tornadoes

D hurricanes

12. The troposphere, mesosphere, and stratosphere are layers of _____ A _____ .

A Earth's atmosphere

B Earth's oceans

C tornadoes

D hurricanes

14. Meteorologists use a(n) _____ D _____ to measure temperature.

A Doppler radar

B weather satellite

C anemometer

D thermometer

Inquiry Skills

15. Infer You hear on the morning weather report that a low-pressure system is approaching. What can you infer about the weather for the day?

It will probably rain, and the temperature may drop.

_____

16. Predict What would happen to ocean surface currents if planetary winds shifted? Describe an example as part of your answer.

Sample answer: A shift in planetary winds would shift

ocean surface currents. This can cause an El Niño.

_____

Critical Thinking

17. Apply What might be the consequence if the ozone layer in the upper stratosphere were completely destroyed? Explain why the ozone layer is important.

Much more ultraviolet radiation would make it to Earth's

surface. The ozone layer protects plants and animals from

harmful rays.

18. Evaluate What would you say to someone who claims that weather forecasters are never right? Give examples in your answer.

Weather forecasting is not perfect. Students should give

examples of accurate and inaccurate forecasts.

19. Analyze Why do you think that meteorologists use computers to analyze weather data?

Computers can compare large amounts of data.

20. Analyze What is the relationship between cloud type and weather? Discuss specific types of clouds in your answer.

Cirrus clouds are associated with pleasant weather. Cumulus

clouds are associated with fair weather. Cumulonimbus clouds

are associated with heavy rain or thunderstorms.

Chapter 12

Vocabulary

Complete each sentence with a term from the list.

1. It takes Earth about one year to make a(n) _____revolution_____ around the Sun.

2. A(n) _____umbra_____ is the dark inner region of an eclipse shadow.

3. The difference between high and low tide is called the _____tidal range_____.

4. When the Sun and the Moon are at right angles relative to Earth, and the Sun's gravitational pull opposes the Moon's, the tides are called _____neap tides_____.

5. Changes in the Moon's appearance as seen from Earth are called _____phases_____.

6. A(n) _____solar eclipse_____ occurs when the Moon aligns between the Sun and Earth.

7. _____Tidal bulges_____ remain aligned with the Moon as Earth rotates.

8. During _____spring tides_____, high tides are extra high.

9. A(n) _____lunar eclipse_____ occurs when Earth aligns between the Sun and the Moon.

10. Areas where the oceans stick out at the sides of Earth are called _____tidal bulges_____.

lunar eclipse D58

neap tides D65

phases D56

revolution D48

rotation D47

solar eclipse D59

spring tides D65

tidal bulges D65

tidal range D66

tides D64

umbra D58

Test Prep

Write the letter of the best answer choice.

11. When Earth, Moon, and Sun line up, and one body moves into the shadow of another, a(n) _____D_____ occurs.

   A phase

   B equinox

   C solstice

   D eclipse

12. The rising and falling of Earth's oceans caused by the Moon's gravitational pull are called _____B_____.

   A eclipses

   B tides

   C phases

   D seasons

13. Earth's _____A_____ about its axis causes day and night.

   A rotation

   B revolution

   C planetary transit

   D apparent motion

14. Earth's tilt and orbit around the Sun together cause the _____C_____.

   A ebb tides

   B phases

   C seasons

   D tidal bulges

Inquiry Skills

15. Compare Study the illustration in your book. Describe what three people at points A, B, and C would see in the sky.

A person at A would see a total eclipse. A person at B would

see a partial eclipse. A person at C would see a no eclipse.

16. Infer You are standing on a rocky beach and you notice a dry rock with seaweed growing on it. Next to the rock is a small pool with a large fish in it. Is it high tide or low tide on the beach? Explain your reasoning.

It is low tide, because the seaweed would be under water

at high tide and because the fish would have found its way

into the pool at high tide.

Critical Thinking

17. Evaluate While doing research, Elise finds a Web site that has this announcement:

Rare Celestial Event!

This month, partial lunar eclipses will occur on December 5 and December 17.

Mark your calendar!

What should Elise conclude?

The Web site does not understand lunar eclipses and the

Moon's orbit. Lunar eclipses cannot occur 12 days apart. They

occur during full Moon phases, which are 29.5 days apart.

_____

18. Apply Compare the clothing you would wear to an outdoor New Year's Eve sky-watching party in your community to the clothes you would probably wear to attend a similar party in Australia.

You would bundle up in warm clothes at home and wear

shorts and a sweatshirt in Australia.

_____

19. Synthesize A coastal area has record high tides. What can you infer about the Moon's phases and the type of tides?

The highest tides occur during spring tides when the Sun, the

Moon, and Earth are aligned—new Moon or full Moon phase.

_____

20. Evaluate Explain whether or not a planetary transit of both Mercury and Venus could occur at the same time.

Due to differences in orbits, it would be a rare occurrence for

Mercury, Venus, and Earth to all align—but it could happen.

_____

Chapter 13

Vocabulary

Complete each sentence with a term from the list.

1. Distances between planets are measured in
   ____astronomical units____ .

2. A(n) ___optical telescope___ is an instrument used to
   see objects that are far away.

3. When you observe the brightness of a star from Earth,
   you are seeing its ___apparent magnitude___ .

4. A(n) _____nebula_____ is a cloud of dust and gas.

5. A(n) ____meteoroid____ is a rocky object that has
   been knocked from its regular orbit.

6. ____Asteroids____ are rocky bodies that have a
   regular orbit around the Sun.

7. ___Absolute magnitude___ is the measure of how much
   light a star gives off.

8. A(n) _____comet_____ is a ball of rock and ice in an irregular
   orbit around the Sun.

9. A(n) _____galaxy_____ consists of old and new stars plus
   dust and gas all held together by gravity.

10. A(n) ____light-year____ is the distance that light travels in one
    year.

asteroids D82

astronomical units
D76

absolute magnitude
D90

apparent magnitude
D90

comet D82

galaxy D95

light-year D95

meteoroid D82

nebula D92

optical telescope D88

Use with pages D100–D101

Test Prep

Write the letter of the best answer choice.

11. Planets stay in orbit around the Sun because of the Sun's ____B____.

A mass

B gravitational force

C solar wind

D heat energy

12. Venus may be similar to Earth in that ____D____.

A its atmosphere has oxygen

B there is liquid water on the surface

C the temperature is moderate

D it has tectonic plates

13. The Milky Way Galaxy is an example of a(n) ____C____ galaxy.

A irregular

B elliptical

C spiral

D barred

14. A star that is stabilized is a ____D____.

A main-sequence star

B neutron star

C nebula

D white dwarf

Inquiry Skills

15. Calculate Jupiter is located 778,412,020 km from the Sun. Earth is located 149,597,890 km from the Sun. Determine whether the distance from Earth to Jupiter and back is less than 1 light-year.

The distance between Earth and Jupiter is 778,412,020 –

149,597,890 = 628,814,130 km. A round trip is

1,257,628,260 km. This is less than 1 light-year, which is

equal to 9.5 trillion km.

16. Compare Compare spiral, elliptical, and irregular galaxies.

All are collections of gas, dust, and stars. Spiral galaxies

have arms that radiate out from a central bulge. Elliptical

galaxies contain very little gas and dust. Irregular galaxies

have no definite structure.

Critical Thinking

17. Analyze Use the terms *apparent magnitude* and *absolute magnitude* to explain how two stars can appear equally bright even though one is much farther away from Earth.

The star that is farther away must have a higher absolute

magnitude. It gives off more light than the closer star that

has the same apparent magnitude.

18. Apply While looking through your telescope, you find that objects appear hazy and unclear. It is not easy to get a clear view of objects that are far away. Someone suggests that you take your telescope to a higher elevation such as a mountaintop. Why would this help?

Clouds, pollution, dust particles, and light pollution all

interfere with viewing. At higher elevations, some or all of

these problems are lessened or absent.

19. Analyze You have learned that the planets can be divided into inner, terrestrial planets and outer, gas giant planets. Based on what you have learned about the Sun and its influence on the planets, explain how you think this division came about.

Sample answer: The Sun burned off most of the gaseous

parts of the inner planets.

20. Hypothesize Most planets closest to the Sun contain carbon dioxide in their atmospheres. The outer planets do not. Instead, most contain hydrogen, helium, and methane. How might their temperatures change if carbon dioxide were part of their atmospheres?

Carbon dioxide keeps heat in the atmosphere by blocking the

exit of ultraviolet rays. The surface temperature of the outer

planets might be warmer if carbon dioxide were present.

Use with pages D100–D101

Chapter 14

Vocabulary

Complete each sentence with a term from the list.

1. A(n) _____ atom _____ is the smallest particle that still has the properties of an element.

2. An atom is made up of a nucleus of protons and neutrons surrounded by moving _____ electrons _____.

3. A nucleus has a positive charge because it contains _____ protons _____.

4. Different _____ isotopes _____ of the same element have different numbers of neutrons in their nuclei.

5. A(n) _____ compound _____ is two or more elements chemically combined.

6. A(n) _____ acid _____ tastes sour and turns blue litmus paper red.

7. The elements are arranged by atomic number in the _____ periodic table _____.

8. A(n) _____ ion _____ is an atom with a positive or negative charge.

9. Earth's atmosphere, a chocolate chip cookie, and granola are each examples of a(n) _____ mixture _____.

10. One _____ molecule _____ of water is made of two hydrogen atoms and one oxygen atom.

acid E36

atom E6

base E37

chemical bond E22

compound E20

electron E6

element E10

ion E8

isotope E8

mixture E28

molecule E23

neutron E6

periodic table E11

pH E38

proton E6

solution E30

Test Prep

Write the letter of the best answer choice.

11. What forms when sugar mixes thoroughly in water? _____D_____

   A a heterogeneous mixture

   B sugar ions

   C acids and bases

   D a solution

12. A(n) acid may have a pH of _____.

   A 1

   B 7

   C 10

   D 16

13. Which of these particles has no charge? _____C_____

   A proton

   B electron

   C neutron

   D ion

14. Carbon, oxygen, and neon are examples of _____D_____.

   A molecules

   B nuclei

   C compounds

   D elements

Inquiry Skills

15. Classify Tanisha left a beaker of unknown, clear liquid in the lab overnight. The next day, she noticed that all of the liquid had evaporated, leaving tiny white crystals in the beaker. Was the liquid a pure substance, a heterogeneous mixture, or a homogeneous mixture?

A homogeneous mixture, because it appeared uniform but

could be separated physically.

16. Infer Ricardo has three solutions, A, B, and C. He tested each solution with litmus paper and made the chart below. Complete the chart to identify each solution.

Solution	Color Change of Litmus Paper	Acid, Base, or Neutral?
A	blue to red	acid
B	no change	acid to neutral
C	red to blue	base

Critical Thinking

17. Analyze What is the relationship between two elements located in the same column on the periodic table?

The two elements have similar chemical properties.

_____

_____

18. Drawing Conclusions A sample of a compound is made up of particles with positive and negative charges. What can you conclude about the type of bonds that hold the particles together?

Ionic bonds hold the particles together.

_____

_____

19. Apply Mark uses lukewarm water, ice, lemons, and sugar to make lemonade. In what order should he add the ingredients to make lemonade as quickly as possible? Explain.

First, dissolve sugar in the water, then squeeze lemon juice

into the water, and then add ice to the water. The lukewarm

water temperature will dissolve the sugar faster than iced

water would.

20. Synthesis Charise used butter, flour, sugar, lemons, vinegar, salt, and baking soda to make cookies. They were very bitter because she added too much of one ingredient. Which ingredient would you conclude she overused?

She overused baking soda.

_____

Chapter 15

Vocabulary

Complete each sentence with a term from the list.

1. A change of state from gas to liquid is called _____condensation_____

2. _____Temperature_____ describes the average kinetic energy of the particles that make up a substance.

3. The amount of force exerted over a certain area is called _____pressure_____.

4. In a(n) _____endothermic reaction_____, energy is absorbed.

5. The _____law of conservation of matter_____ states that matter cannot be created or destroyed.

6. In a(n) _____exothermic reaction_____, energy is released.

7. A change in size due to a change in temperature is _____thermal expansion_____.

8. _____Thermal energy_____ describes the total kinetic energy of the particles of a sample.

9. A(n) _____chemical equation_____ describes the changes that occur during a chemical reaction.

10. A liquid will undergo _____vaporization_____ at its boiling point.

chemical change E60

chemical equation E68

chemical reaction E62

condensation E54

endothermic reaction E63

exothermic reaction E64

law of conservation of matter E71

pressure E52

temperature E51

thermal energy E51

thermal expansion E51

vaporization E54

volume E52

Use with pages E76–E77

Name _____ Date _____

Test Prep
Write the letter of the best answer choice.

11. In a _____C_____ reaction, one element replaces another element in a compound.

   A synthesis

   B decomposition

   C single-replacement

   D double-replacement

12. What kind of reaction is described by the following chemical equation?

   _____D_____

   $CaCO_3 + 2HCl \rightarrow CaCl_2 + H_2CO_3$

   A synthesis

   B decomposition

   C single-replacement

   D double-replacement

13. Which of the following terms is used to describe what happens when a hot piece of metal increases in size?

   _____C_____

   A vaporization

   B thermal energy

   C thermal expansion

   D temperature

14. If the temperature of a container holding a gas is kept constant, the pressure of the gas will _____B_____ as the volume decreases.

   A decrease

   B increase

   C stay the same

   D equal the volume

Inquiry Skills

15. **Hypothesize** What will happen to a balloon that is filled with warm air and then placed in the freezer? Explain your answer.

   The volume of air inside the balloon will decrease as the

   temperature decreases, causing the balloon to shrink in size.

16. **Compare** Reaction A involves two substances combining to form one new substance. Reaction B involves one substance breaking down into two substances. Name these two reactions.

   Reaction A

   $2Ca + O_2 \rightarrow 2CaO$

   Reaction B

   $2HgO \rightarrow 2Hg + O_2$

   A: synthesis, B: decomposition

Critical Thinking

17. Evaluate Why is it dangerous to place a container holding a pressurized gas near an open flame or other heat source?

When the pressurized gas in the container is heated, the

pressure will increase if the volume of the container cannot

increase. The pressure inside the container might get high

enough for the container to burst.

18. Analyze Carlos is removing energy from a sample of gas in a closed container. The temperature of the sample decreases steadily from 10:05 A.M. to 10:25 A.M. From 10:25 A.M. to 10:28 A.M., the sample remains at one temperature. From 10:28 A.M. to 10:39 A.M., the temperature decreases steadily again. Explain what is happening in the container from 10:25 A.M. to 10:28 A.M.

Between 10:25 A.M. and 10:28 A.M., the substance is

condensing, changing from a gas to a liquid. As energy

is removed, the temperature of the sample will remain the

same while a change of state is occurring.

19. Apply Gasoline consists mainly of hydrocarbons, compounds made of carbon and hydrogen. When gasoline burns in the presence of oxygen in a car engine, a combustion reaction is taking place. What two substances are produced by the reaction?

Carbon dioxide and water are produced.

20. Synthesize Some hot packs get very warm when you mix the chemicals inside them. What type of chemical reaction is likely taking place?

The chemicals inside the hot pack are likely undergoing an

exothermic reaction, because energy is being released.

Chapter 16

Vocabulary

Complete each sentence with a term from the list. You may use each term more than once.

1. Energy is measured in units called _____joules_____.

2. The _law of conservation of energy_ states that energy can change form but it cannot be created or destroyed.

3. The higher the _____frequency_____, the shorter the wavelength of a wave.

4. A sound wave in air is a(n) _longitudinal wave_.

5. Energy of motion is called _____kinetic energy_____.

6. A sound's pitch is related to its _____frequency_____.

7. Two objects that are in contact and have the same temperature are said to be in _thermal equilibrium_.

8. Thermal energy is transferred through a metal spoon by _____conduction_____.

9. _____Heat_____ is thermal energy transferred from objects at higher temperature to objects at lower temperature.

10. A(n) _____insulator_____ conducts thermal energy poorly.

amplitude F15

conduction F26

conductor F27

convection F26

fission F10

frequency F15

fusion F10

heat F25

hertz F15

insulator F27

joules F6

kinetic energy F8

law of conservation of energy F7

longitudinal wave F15

potential energy F8

radiation F27

thermal equilibrium F25

transverse wave F15

wave F14

wavelength F15

Test Prep

Write the letter of the best answer choice.

11. Conduction, convection, and radiation are all ways that ____B____ can be transferred.

A electricity

B thermal energy

C water

D gases

12. All forms of energy can be described as either ____C____.

A chemical or electrical energy

B mechanical or thermal energy

C kinetic or potential energy

D stationary or gravitational energy

13. All waves EXCEPT ____A____ need a medium to move through.

A electromagnetic waves

B sound waves

C water waves

D earthquake waves

14. Three properties of waves are ____D____.

A rarefaction, reflection, and wavelength

B compression, rarefaction, and pitch

C amplitude, longitude, and latitude

D wavelength, frequency, and amplitude

Inquiry Skills

15. Compare Define *kinetic energy* and *potential energy* in terms of the example shown in the photo in your book.

At the top of the peak, the climber has a lot of potential

energy. As he begins moving down the peak, the potential

energy is converted to kinetic energy.

16. Use Models Look at the diagrams of sound waves on page F16. How are they like real sound waves? How are they different?

They are compressed longitudinal waves. Sound waves

travel in all directions from a point, however.

_____

Use with pages F32–F33

Critical Thinking

17. **Apply** Name some types of waves that you might encounter during the day. In what kinds of places might you find these waves?

Types of waves encountered during the day are sound

waves, water waves, and light waves.

_____

18. **Synthesize** What kinds of materials would you use to make a device that could conduct heat well? For what types of tasks might you use such a device?

Sample answer: Metals conduct heat very well. A slab of

copper that is heated in the oven could serve as a hot pad

to keep food warm on the dinner table.

_____

19. **Evaluate** A newspaper editorial on a proposed nuclear power plant in your community contains this statement: "A nuclear reaction does not simply release energy; it creates energy where none existed before." Write a brief response to this statement.

Sample answer: The law of conservation of energy states

that energy cannot be created or destroyed. The statement

in the editorial is incorrect.

_____

20. **Analyze** How is radiation related to electromagnetic waves and thermal energy?

Electromagnetic waves transfer thermal energy through

radiation.

Use with pages F32–F33

Name _____ Date _____

Chapter 17

Vocabulary

Complete each sentence with a term from the list.

1. A(n) _____opaque_____ material does not let light rays pass through.

2. The colors of the rainbow make up the _____visible spectrum_____.

3. A(n) _____incandescent_____ light bulb uses a heated filament to produce light.

4. The bending of light as it passes from one material to another is called _____refraction_____.

5. Radio waves and gamma waves are part of the _____electromagnetic spectrum_____.

6. A(n) _____laser_____ produces a narrow beam of light of one color.

7. A(n) _____convex_____ mirror curves outward and spreads light rays apart.

8. Light can easily pass through a(n) _____transparent_____ material.

9. A(n) _____electromagnetic wave_____ is made up of electric and a magnetic fields.

10. A(n) _____fluorescent_____ lamp emits light by exciting gases.

coherent light F42
concave F53
convex F53
electromagnetic waves F38
electromagnetic spectrum F38
fluorescent F40
incandescent F40
laser F42
lens F55
opaque F51
reflection F52
refraction F54
translucent 51
transparent F51
visible spectrum F56

Test Prep

Write the letter of the best answer choice.

11. _____C_____ occurs when light bounces off the surface of an object.

   A Absorption

   B Incidence

   C Reflection

   D Refraction

12. A(n) _____C_____ material scatters the light rays that it lets through.

   A opaque

   B shiny

   C translucent

   D transparent

13. The color of an object that you see is the wavelengths of light _____B_____ by that object.

   A refracted

   B reflected

   C filtered

   D absorbed

14. Laser light is _____B_____.

   A incandescent

   B coherent

   C opaque

   D always red

Inquiry Skills

15. **Hypothesize** The face of a diamond is cut into a number of small surfaces at different angles. The diamond sparkles when viewed from the front, but is dull when viewed from behind. Hypothesize why different parts of the diamond sparkle or do not sparkle. Give reasons.

   The diamond is cut so that the flat surfaces reflect most

   of the light rays that hit them. The back is not cut, so it does

   not reflect the light as much and appears dull.

16. **Infer** Kyle tested different mirrors for the fun house he was designing. Kyle decided to use three different mirrors—one that did not distort objects, one that made objects look taller, and one that made objects look much smaller. What can you infer about these mirrors?

   not curved: did not distort objects, concave: made objects

   taller, convex: made objects smaller

Critical Thinking

17. Analyze Yvette spotted an object that appeared to be about a meter away on the bottom of a clear shallow pool. When she reached in to get the object, she realized that the actual position of the object was closer to the edge of the pool than she had thought. Explain.

The light rays from the object are bent as they travel from water to air. The eyes see the object in a position that is different from the actual position.

18. Analyze Explain why rainbows are often seen during a brief shower.

The Sun is still shining in the sky during a brief shower, and the raindrops act like prisms.

19. Apply The road leading to Shawna's farm is L-shaped. There is a tall fence that blocks all views, so approaching cars cannot be seen around the L-shaped corner. Describe how she might solve the problem.

Place a large plane or convex mirror facing the corner so that the front of the mirror can be seen by cars on both approaches toward the corner. The cars will see a reflection of objects around the corner.

20. Synthesize Explain why white clothing will keep you cooler in summer than black clothing.

White reflects nearly all the light falling on it, and black absorbs nearly all the light falling on it. Light that is absorbed converts to heat, so the absorbed light in black clothing makes you warmer.

Use with pages F64–F65

Chapter 18

Vocabulary

Complete each sentence with a term from the list.

1. The flow of electric charges creates
   __current electricity__ .

2. Electric charges do not move easily through a(n)
   ___insulator___ .

3. A(n) __electric generator__ converts mechanical
   energy into electric energy.

4. ___Electricity___ , a form of energy, may involve
   static or moving charges.

5. The pull or push of a magnet is felt in an area around
   it, called the __magnetic field__ .

6. __Static electricity__ is a buildup of charge on a
   material.

7. Current in a conductor wrapped around an iron core produces
   a(n) __electromagnet__ .

8. In a(n) ___circuit___ , moving charges follow a pathway.

9. A(n) __electric motor__ is a device that changes electric
   energy to mechanical energy.

10. Electric wires are made of copper because copper is a good
    __conductor__ .

circuit F71

conductor F76

current electricity F71

electric generator F84

electric motor F85

electricity F70

electromagnet F83

insulator F76

magnetic field F83

magnetism F82

static electricity F71

Test Prep

Write the letter of the best answer choice.

11. What is the property of iron, but not copper or zinc? _____A_____

    A magnetism

    B electric conduction

    C electric insulation

    D current electricity

12. Which device converts electric energy into sound energy? _____D_____

    A cathode ray tube

    B electric motor

    C electric generator

    D electric speaker

13. A wire that cuts across a magnet's lines of force _____A_____.

    A has an induced current

    B creates mechanical energy

    C creates magnetic energy

    D completes a parallel circuit

14. A transformer _____D_____.

    A converts one form of energy into another

    B changes electrical impulses into sound waves

    C is usually used with DC current

    D converts current with one voltage to current with a different voltage

Inquiry Skills

15. Infer The manual that comes with a clothes dryer says that it must not be plugged into an extension cord. The manual for a radio does not include any such warning. How would you explain this difference?

The clothes dryer operates at a higher voltage than a radio.

It draws more current from the outlet, heating up its special

thick cord. An extension cord would get overheated by the

high current.

_____

_____

_____

16. Hypothesize Why do you think a magnet attracts a Canadian nickel but not an American nickel?

The amount of nickel, a magnetic material, is greater in a

Canadian nickel.

Critical Thinking

17. Apply What might happen if you plug several appliances into one outlet? Describe how the circuits in your home would be affected.

The total voltage of the appliances might be more than the

outlet can supply. The circuit could shut down.

18. Evaluate What type of circuit would you expect to find in a string of holiday lights? Explain.

A parallel circuit; if one bulb burns out, the others will

remain lit.

19. Synthesize What might be the advantage of using several small power stations in a region rather than one or two large ones? Describe different events that might support your answer.

Sample answer: Less energy is lost in transmitting

electricity over shorter distances.

20. Analyze Why does a stereo speaker use alternating current rather than direct current? Explain your reasoning.

Alternating current makes the magnetic fields from the

voice coil change direction, with the result that the cone

moves back and forth and sets up sound waves.

Chapter 19

Vocabulary

Complete each sentence with a term from the list.

1. _____inertia_____ is the tendency for objects at rest to stay at rest and objects in motion to stay in motion.

2. Distance divided by time equals _____speed_____.

3. A lever, an inclined plane, or a pulley is an example of a(n) ____simple machine____.

4. The _____weight_____ of an object depends on its mass and the force of gravity.

5. The force of _____friction_____ opposes motion of one surface across another.

6. The speed and direction of an object describe its _____velocity_____.

7. The unit of force is called a(n) _____newton_____.

8. The amount of matter in an object is the _____mass_____ of the object.

9. The ____efficiency____ of a machine is a ratio that is always less than 100 percent.

10. The three laws that describe the relationship between motion and force are ____Newton's laws of motion____.

acceleration F100

efficiency F123

frame of reference F102

friction F108

gravity F113

inertia F106

mass F114

mechanical advantage F123

newton F107

Newton's laws of motion F106

simple machine F123

speed F98

velocity F100

weight F114

Use with pages F133–F134

Test Prep

Write the letter of the best answer choice.

11. The rate at which velocity changes is
_____.

   A acceleration

   B average speed

   C distance

   D speed

12. How fast a train appears to move depends on the observer's
_____.

   A gravity

   B weight

   C mass

   D frame of reference

13. Objects accelerate as they fall to Earth because of _____.

   A gravity

   B inertia

   C mechanical advantage

   D simple machines

14. Speeding up, slowing down, and changing direction are each an example of _____.

   A constant velocity

   B constant speed

   C constant position

   D acceleration

Inquiry Skills

15. Experiment A ball is at rest in the middle of a flat car on a moving train. When the train turns to the left, will the ball begin to roll? If so, in which direction? Form a hypothesis. Describe how you could test it.

Sample answer: It will roll to the right side of the car. This _____

can be tested with a marble and a model train. _____

16. Draw Conclusions Inventors sometimes try to build a perpetual motion machine, which is a machine that keeps moving forever without work done to it. Do you think such a machine is possible? Why or why not?

Sample answer: No, all machines lose energy to friction. _____

Without work done to it, the machine will slow down and _____

eventually stop. _____

Use with pages F133–F134

Critical Thinking

17. Analyze Juan put his drink on the dashboard of his mother's car. When the car started moving, the drink fell off. Explain why.

The drink remained at rest when the car moved forward.

The dashboard moved forward with the car (away from the

drink), causing the drink to fall.

18. Synthesize Suppose you wanted to lift a heavy object up high to a tree house. Describe a way you could use simple machines to do so. Explain your choice of machines.

Sample answer: Create a moveable pulley system with many

sections so that each section shares the weight of the object.

19. Apply What could you do to make snow skis or a toboggan go faster or farther down a hill? Explain.

Sample answer: Reduce friction between the snow and the

bottom of the skis or toboggan by rubbing a substance

(such as wax) that reduces the friction on the bottom of the

skis or toboggan.

20. Evaluate A common belief among drivers is that a truck requires more distance to stop than a small car does. Do you agree or disagree? Explain why.

A truck has more mass than a car. Force is mass multiplied

by acceleration, so acceleration is force divided by mass.

If the forces are the same, then a larger mass has less

acceleration. Therefore, it will take a larger mass a longer

time to stop, and thus a longer distance.

Unit A

Circle the correct letter.

1. A particular multicellular organism neither makes nor eats food. This organism is classified in which kingdom?

   A Animalia

   (B) Fungi

   C Plantae

   D Protista

2. Which of the following is a non-vascular plant?

   A

   Maple Tree

   C

   Grass

   B

   Daisy

   (D)
   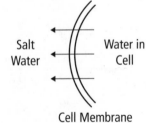
   Moss

3. What causes infectious diseases?

   A poor nutrition

   B lack of exercise

   (C) viruses and bacteria

   D inherited conditions

4. The diagram illustrates which process?

   A active transport

   B mitosis

   (C) photosynthesis

   D osmosis

   Salt Water   Water in Cell
   Cell Membrane

5. The diagram shows a stage in the process of

   A infection.

   B fertilization.

   C interphase.

   D mitosis.

6. Which statement about RNA is NOT true?

   A It forms one strand.

   B One of its bases is uracil.

   C It builds up to form genes.

   D It is used to create proteins.

7. Which geological era is characterized by the following?

> • dinosaurs appear
>
> • mammals become widespread
>
> • flowering plants appear

   A Cenozoic

   B Mesozoic

   C Paleozoic

   D Precambrian

8. What contains the coded information of a molecule of DNA?

   A the number of different base pairs

   B the specific order of base pairs

   C the size of base pairs

   D the number of "twists" in the double helix

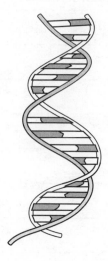

Student Resources

Use with pages A142–A143

Answer the following in complete sentences.

9. Name the two basic types of symmetry found in the animal kingdom. Give two examples of each type.

Sample answer:

Radial: starfish, sand dollars (also some

sponges); Bilateral: butterfly, horse

_____

_____

_____

_____

10. There are four basic human blood types: A, B, AB, and O. The Punnett square shows the possible allele combinations for the offspring from two people, one with Type A blood and one with Type B blood. The Type A person carries the A and O alleles. The Type B person carries the B and O alleles. There is a 1 in 4 chance of these alleles producing a child with blood type AB or O. What does this tell you about the A and B alleles and the O allele?

| | Type A Person | |
	A	O
Type B Person B	AB	BO
Type B Person O	AO	OO

The A and B alleles are codominant. Together they

produce

blood type AB. The O allele is recessive. Two Os are needed

to produce blood type O.

_____

_____

_____

_____

Unit B

Circle the correct letter.

1. Which process is illustrated here?

   A cellular respiration

   B oxygen cycle

   C photosynthesis

   D transpiration

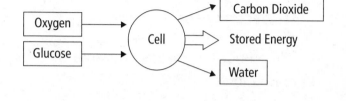

2. Which is the energy source for plants and algae?

   A primary consumers

   B secondary consumers

   C the sun

   D producers

3. Which term below includes the other three terms?

   A biome

   B ecosystem

   C biotic factors

   D abiotic factors

4. Look at the food web. Which statement about the food web is true?

   A The bear is a producer.

   B The fish is a primary consumer.

   C The water plants, fish, and berries form a food chain.

   D The bear and raccoon fill exactly the same niche.

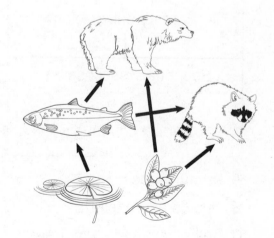

Use with pages B94–B95

5. What is part of the niche that a raccoon fills in an ecosystem?

   A carnivore

   (B) omnivore

   C herbivore

   D decomposer

6. Which ocean zone is characterized by warm, shallow water that is rich in nutrients?

   A intertidal zone

   B shoreline zone

   C oceanic zone

   (D) neritic zone

7. The amount of water in an ecosystem could be an example of a

   A biotic factor.

   (B) limiting factor.

   C carrying capacity.

   D spike and dip cycle.

8. The diagram below shows the steps in the ecological succession of devastated land. Which organisms are characteristic of the primary succession stage?

```
┌─────────────────────────────┐
│      Primary succession       │
│              ↓                │
│     Secondary succession      │
│              ↓                │
│       Climax community        │
└─────────────────────────────┘
```

   A mature trees

   (B) molds and bacteria

   C tall plants and small trees

   D fast-growing grasses and weeds

Answer the following in complete sentences.

9. Explain the function of bacteria and fungi in the nitrogen cycle.

Certain kinds of bacteria and fungi break down nitrogen
compounds in animal waste products and in dead animals
and plants. As a result, nitrogen compounds are returned
to the soil. Other kinds of bacteria change nitrogen
compounds in the soil to pure nitrogen, which goes into the
air.

10. Explain the relationship between mutualism, commensalism, and parasitism.

All three are types of symbiosis, a close relationship
between two species. In a symbiotic relationship, at least
one of the species benefits from the relationship. In
mutualism, both species benefit. In commensalism, one
species benefits. The other is neither helped nor harmed. In
parasitism, one species benefits and the other is harmed.

Unit C

Circle the correct letter.

1. The Mohs scale is used to measure which property of minerals?

   A cleavage

   B hardness

   C luster

   D streak

2. The illustration shows the boundary between two tectonic plates. As these plates move, which is MOST likely to happen?

   A Mountains will form.

   B Plains will form.

   C Magma will create new crust.

   D An underwater trench will form.

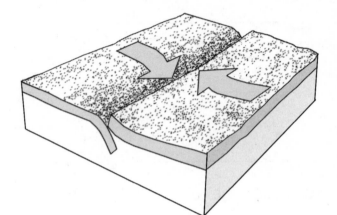

3. Which is an example of nonrenewable energy?

   A fossil fuels

   B geothermal energy

   C solar energy

   D wind energy

4. Plants from the Carboniferous period help form today's

   A fossil fuels.

   B rocks.

   C soils.

   D minerals.

Use with pages C94–C95

5. Which is NOT true of minerals?

A They occur naturally.

B They have crystal structures.

C They are made only of metals.

D They are made of compounds.

6. Which has a definite chemical composition and physical structure?

A feldspar

B granite

C marble

D sandstone

7. Which process or processess created the rock formation shown below?

A sedimentation

B volcanic activity

C weathering and erosion

D heating and rapid cooling

8. Rock that is formed when molten rock cools and hardens is classified as _____.

A crystals.

B igneous.

C metamorphic.

D sedimentary.

Name _____ Date _____

Answer the following in complete sentences.

9. Scientists have found fossils of the same freshwater fish on opposite shores of the Atlantic Ocean. Explain how this supports the theory of continental drift.

Sample answer: The fossils are of freshwater fish, but the

ocean is salt water. These fish could not have crossed the

salty ocean. If the theory of continental drift is correct,

the two opposite shores of the Atlantic were once joined

together and then slowly drifted apart. This would account

for the identical fossils on opposite sides of the ocean.

_____

_____

10. The Appalachian Mountains are low and rounded. The Rocky Mountains are high and jagged. Which mountain range is older? Explain your answer.

Appalachian Mountains

Rocky Mountains

Sample answer: The Appalachian

Mountains. The rounded shape of the

Appalachians is evidence of erosion.

The Rocky Mountains have sharp,

jagged peaks. Not as much

erosion has occurred here, so they must be younger than

the Appalachians.

_____

_____

Unit D

Circle the correct letter.

1. The boundary between two air masses is called a

   A front.

   B stratus.

   C sea breeze.

   D convection current.

2. Great Britain and Nova Scotia are about the same distance north of the equator. Which causes Great Britain to be much warmer than Nova Scotia?

   A Coriolis effect

   B El Niño

   C Gulf Stream

   D greenhouse effect

3. Which weather event begins as a low-pressure system over warm tropical waters?

   A blizzard

   B hurricane

   C thunderstorm

   D tornado

4. Which arrangement of the Sun, Earth, and the Moon will result in a solar eclipse?

   A

   C

   B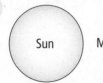

   D

Use with pages D102–D103

5. The main cause of the ocean's tides is

   A the pull of Earth's gravity on the oceans.

   B the pull of the Moon's gravity on the oceans.

   C magnetic forces from Earth's iron core.

   D electrical forces from the Moon.

6. The diagram below illustrates which distance?

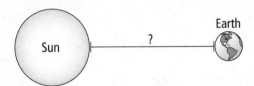

   A 1 light-year

   B a planetary unit

   C 1 astronomical unit

   D 150 kilometers (km)

7. A person in his or her backyard looking at the stars could observe a star's

   A absolute magnitude.

   B apparent magnitude.

   C galaxy.

   D real size.

8. What will be the next stage in the following sequence?

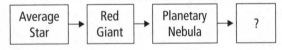

   A black hole

   B supernova

   C neutron star

   D white dwarf

Answer the following in complete sentences.

9. Describe the importance of ozone in Earth's atmosphere.

Ozone is found in a layer of the atmosphere called the

stratosphere. It absorbs harmful ultraviolet light from the

Sun.

10. Every four years, one day is added to the calendar to create a leap year. Explain why this is necessary.

Earth's orbit around the Sun is slightly longer than 365

days by about 6 hours. Over four years, this adds up to

24 hours, or one day. Every four years, we add a day to

the calendar so the calendar will stay in line with Earth's

movement around the Sun.

Unit E

Circle the correct letter.

1. Which substance is NOT a solution?

   A brass

   B concrete

   C steel

   D sugar water

2. An element's atomic number is determined by

   A the mass of a single atom.

   B the mass of a single nucleus.

   C the number of protons in one atom.

   D the number of neutrons in one atom.

3. The table below shows the first three elements in group 7A.
   Which of the following is true about the elements?

   A Chlorine is a liquid at room temperature.

   B Fluorine has the greatest atomic number.

   C They have similar chemical properties.

   D They belong to a group called the noble gases.

7A
9 **F** Fluorine
17 **Cl** Chlorine
35 **Br** Bromine

4. Which equation shows a synthesis reaction?

   A $4Fe + 3O_2 \rightarrow 2Fe_2O_3$

   B $2C_2H_2 + 5O_2 \rightarrow 4CO_2 + 2H_2O$

   C $C_6H_{12}O_6 + 6O_2 \rightarrow 6O_2 + 6H_2O$

   D $2H_2O \rightarrow 2H_2 + O_2$

5. Which diagram shows a molecule made from one element?

A

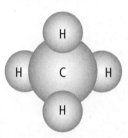

C

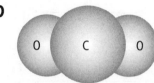

B

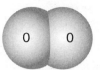

D

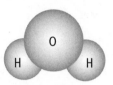

6. Chemical changes either absorb or release

A atoms.

C molecules.

B energy.

D protons.

7. All of the sealed plastic containers shown were originally the same shape. They now contain the same amount of the same gas. In which container is the gas at the LOWEST temperature?

A    **B**    **C**    **D**

8. Scientists today prefer the electron cloud model of the atom to Bohr's model because it

A indicates that the electrons orbit the nucleus of the atom.

B indicates that the exact location of the electrons is unknown.

C shows that the nucleus contains both protons and neutrons.

D shows that the electrons surround the nucleus of the atom.

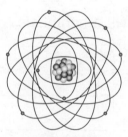

Bohr's Model

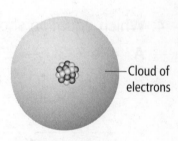

—Cloud of electrons

Electron Cloud Model

Use with pages E78–E79

Answer the following in complete sentences.

9. Explain the difference between covalent and ionic bonds.

The atoms in a covalent bond share electrons. The shared

electrons form a bond that holds the atoms together in a

molecule. In an ionic bond, electrons from one atom move

to another atom. The atom that gave up electrons is now

a positive ion. The atom that gained electrons is now a

negative ion. The positive and negative charges of the ions

attract each other and hold the ions together.

10. The chemical equation below shows the reaction that takes place in photosynthesis. Is this reaction endothermic or exothermic? Explain your answer.

$6CO_2 + 6H_2O \rightarrow C_6H_{12}O_6 + 6O_2$

Endothermic; The reaction is endothermic because it is

a reaction in which energy is absorbed. The energy is

absorbed from the Sun.

Name _____ Date _____

Unit F

Circle the correct letter.

1. Which is the most powerful source of energy?

   A elastic energy

   B nuclear energy

   C chemical energy

   D mechanical energy

2. The illustration below represents a sound wave. If the distance *x* increases, the sound will

   A become louder.

   B become softer.

   C go up in pitch.

   D go down in pitch.

   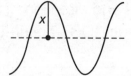

3. Which light source produces "coherent light"?

   A fluorescent

   B incandescent

   C laser

   D phosphorescent

4. The diagram below shows a prism refracting white light. Which light rays are refracted at the greatest angle?

   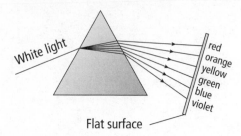

   A red rays

   B violet rays

   C green rays

   D yellow rays

Use with pages E134–E135

Name _____ Date _____

5. Which simple machine does NOT increase the amount of force applied?

A

B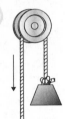

C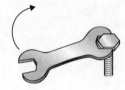

D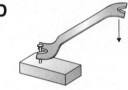

6. The illustration shows the speed and direction of two planes at a given moment. Which statement MOST accurately describes their movement?

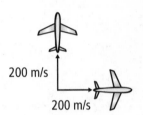
200 m/s
200 m/s

A The planes have the same velocity but different speeds.

B The planes have the same speed but different velocities.

C The planes have the same acceleration but different speeds.

D The planes have the same velocity but different accelerations.

7. The contact force that opposes the motion of one surface against another is called

A friction.

B gravity.

C inertia.

D weight.

8. Which device transforms mechanical energy into electrical energy?

A motor

B cathode ray tube

C electromagnet

D generator

Name _____ Date _____

Answer the following in complete sentences.

9. A cup of hot water and a cup of ice water sit on a table in an 80°F room. Describe how the temperature of the water in the cups will change in terms of thermal equilibrium.

Thermal energy, or heat, from the hot water will move from

the hot liquid into the cooler room. Thermal energy from

the air in the room will warm the ice water. Eventually, the

water in the cups and the air will reach the point of thermal

equilibrium. At this point, their temperatures will be the

same.

_____

_____

_____

10. Noelle hooked up the two circuits shown. She makes these two observations:

• The bulbs in the circuit on the left are very dim.
• The bulbs in the circuit on the right shine with equal brightness.

Explain why the bulbs in the circuit shine differently.

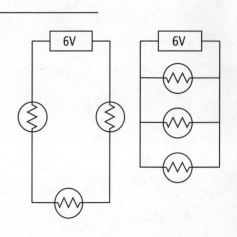

The circuit on the left is a series circuit. In a

series circuit, the voltage decreases from bulb

to bulb because each bulb converts a small portion of the

energy into light energy. The circuit on the right is a parallel

circuit. Each bulb receives the full voltage of the circuit.

_____

_____

_____

_____